The Illustrated Library of

NATURE

VOLUME 9

MAMMALS–(cont.)

NATURE HOBBIES

The American Museum of Natural History

Cooperated in the publication
of this edition.

The Illustrated Library of
NATURE

*T*HIS PICTORIAL ENCYCLOPEDIA of natural history and ecology depicts the relationships of all living organisms to each other and between them and their environments. Original manuscript from the *Doubleday Nature Programs* plus new articles and illustrations are included in this edition.

H. S. STUTTMAN CO., INC., Publishers
New York, N. Y., 10016

Contents

VOLUME 9

MAMMALS–(cont.)

MAMMALS OF EUROPE 1030
► One can fully appreciate the many species that range all across Europe and Asia by considering the continents' land masses and past history.

MONKEYS AND APES 1062
► These primates stayed close to their original homes and were forced to develop agility and coordination.

LITTLE-KNOWN MAMMALS 1092
► There are a surprising number of strange creatures on this planet which are known mostly to zoologists.

NATURE HOBBIES

AQUARIUM FISHES 1124
► A whole miniature water world within four transparent walls for delightful observation.

▶ *One can fully appreciate the many species that range all across Europe and Asia by considering the continents' land masses and past history.*

Mammals of Europe

I<small>T IS NOT POSSIBLE</small> fully to understand Europe's mammals without first considering the continent's physical relations with neighboring land masses, and to some extent its past history. Europe is continuous with Asia to its east, with a long frontier largely marked by the Ural Mountains. To the south of this mountain chain, however, there is no obstacle to the free passage of land animals. Naturally, therefore, many species range across all of Europe and Asia, and a few are found from the British Isles to Japan.

To the south Europe is bounded by the Mediterranean Sea, which separates it from Africa. Yet the mammals of the northern strip of Africa include species found in Europe, including the red fox and the Barbary stag, which is a variety of the red deer. Conversely, a few animals typical of the African fauna, such as the crested porcupine and the bush cat, are found in parts of southern Europe.

Europe has a long coastline in relation to its surface area, with islands more numerous than is usual around a continent. These were once part of the mainland but became separated at various times in the past. Britain, for example, was finally separated from continental Europe about 10,000 years ago, whereas Ireland was almost certainly separated from Britain earlier than this.

When, during the last Ice Age, the ice sheet migrated south to cover the northern half of Europe, the mammals retreated before it. As the ice retreated north again the mammals migrated north, but not all moved at the same time. Some reached Britain before the separation, but others

Of the 184 distinct species of mammals found in Europe, two species, the tarpan, or wild horse, and the aurochs, or wild ox, are now extinct, and eleven species were introduced from other parts of the world. Of the 184, there are eight species of seals and thirty-one species of whales, including the dolphins. The **common seal** (top right) is the smaller of the two seals that are found most abundantly in European coastal waters. The **common dolphin** (top, far right), a fast swimmer, is often seen following ships at sea.

MEL HUNTER

(above)
Similar in appearance to the North American species, the European **brown bear** may cover great distances quickly, mostly during the night. It is fond of bathing in lakes and rivers, and prefers to live alone.

(above, right)
A hind waits in the background as two stags check for possible dangers. Like most other deer, **red deer** are extremely wary and are not often seen except at night. Somewhat smaller than the related North American wapiti, they generally rest and sleep during the day.

The skill of the **ibex,** or **wild goat,** in moving about open, precipitous mountainsides made it a favorite object of sport. Its long horns were coveted as trophies by the hunter, with the result that it was brought very near to extermination in many areas.

failed to do so. Of those that reached Britain, some passed across to Ireland but others failed to reach it. Today, therefore, there are fewer species of mammals in Ireland than in Britain, and fewer in Britain than on continental Europe. Moreover, during the 10,000 years since these changes occurred, the mammals isolated on islands have undergone genetic changes to produce subspecies. For example, the red squirrel of Europe is frequently black, a melanistic variation. The red squirrel in Britain is a subspecies that produces black individuals only rarely but is marked by an habitual pigment change in winter, when the tail goes white. The only red squirrels in Ireland have almost certainly been introduced.

Similar degrees of difference can be found between mammals on the Mediterranean islands and mainland Europe.

Close Relatives from Different Lands

IT MUST BE REMEMBERED that eastern Asia and Alaska were once joined at the present site of the Bering Strait, and many mammals were once continuous across Europe, Asia and North America. Since the separation, genetic changes have produced minor differences (and historical changes have produced differences in names), so that the moose and the European elk are separate but closely related species, as are the reindeer and the caribou, while the North American wapiti is a larger version of the European red deer. Beaver, otter, wolf, brown bear, lynx and others are each represented by North American and by Eurasian species, but they are so closely alike that they could almost be treated as subspecies rather than species.

There is, however, one important difference between European and North American rodents. Both continents have their small rodents, but those in Europe belong to the subfamily Murinae (true rats and mice) except for the voles, lemmings and hamsters, which belong to the sub-

families Microtinae and Cricetinae. The New World rats and mice all belong to the subfamily Cricetinae. The North American harvest mouse is a cricetine, while the European harvest mouse is a murine; yet both look and behave very much alike. The differences between them are mainly anatomical.

The total number of mammals now listed for Europe is 184, but this includes the tarpan, or wild horse, which did not survive the nineteenth century, and the aurochs, or wild ox, that became extinct in the Middle Ages. The Chillingham Herd of white cattle in England is said to be a remnant of the aurochs, but this cannot be satisfactorily proven. The number also includes eleven species accidentally or deliberately introduced from other parts of the world. These are the North American gray squirrel, the muskrat from North America and the coypu from South America, the raccoon dog from eastern Asia, the Japanese sika deer, the Chinese muntjac and the Chinese water deer, the North American raccoon and mink, the Indian buffalo and the musk-ox.

Of the total of 184, there are eight species of seals and thirty-one species of whales, but since none of these marine animals is exclusively European, they will not be considered here.

The Barbary ape, a species of monkey, is found on Gibraltar. It is usually included in the list of European mammals although it is native to north-west Africa and lives on Gibraltar, where it was introduced, in a state of semi-domestication. Otherwise, the only primates native to Europe are human beings.

Shrews, Moles, Desmans and Hedgehogs

THE MOST PRIMITIVE ORDER OF MAMMALS is the Insectivora, which includes shrews and moles, desmans and hedgehogs. This order is represented in Europe by sixteen species, ten of which are shrews. These are all small, most of them mouse-sized, with pointed muzzles,

(above, left)
Now an extinct species, the **tarpan,** or **wild horse,** disappeared nearly a hundred years ago from its home on the steppes of southern Russia.

(above)
Brought to Europe from Asia, the **Indian** (or **water) buffalo** has a liking for swamps and bogs, where it wallows in the mud. When domesticated, it is used for drawing plows and carts. In addition, it is highly valued as a source of rich milk.

Although some mystery still shrouds the **Barbary ape** of the Rock of Gibraltar, it is certainly an African species that was introduced there some time ago. About as large as a medium-sized dog, it is the only monkey living in a semiwild state in Europe.

short legs, a tail usually shorter than the body, with a close fur and small eyes and ears hidden in the fur. They live in the leaf litter or in surface tunnels in the ground, feeding on insects or any similar small animals. The common shrew, about four inches in total length, is the most numerous of Europe's mammals. The pygmy shrew is three and one-half inches and weighs one-fifth of an ounce, and Savi's pygmy shrew of the Mediterranean region, only two and one-half inches overall, is believed by many to be the smallest of all living mammals. The largest European shrews are the two species of water shrew, five and one-half inches in total length.

The Insectivora are so-named not because they necessarily eat insects, but because their teeth are of the kind most suitable for this activity. They have numerous sharp teeth divided into incisors, canines, premolars and molars, all with pointed cusps. The shrews are similar in size and dentition to some of the earliest mammals known, whose fossils date back 200 million years.

Moles, near relatives of shrews, are specially adapted for burrowing, and, although they have teeth like shrews, they feed almost exclusively on earthworms. There are two species, the northern and the Mediterranean mole, both about seven inches long including a short tail. The only differences between them are in slight details in the skull. The very tiny eyes of the Mediterranean mole are sometimes covered with skin; this has given rise to the idea that moles are blind. The snout in both species is long and tapering, the fur is without "set", which means it can be brushed either way without appearing dishevelled, and the front paws are broad. These, with their stout claws, are the digging organs.

The two species of desmans, although allied to moles, look more like large aquatic shrews. The Pyrenean desman, eleven inches long, of which one half is tail, lives in the mountain streams of Portugal, Spain and Pyrenean France. The Russian desman, seventeen inches long, lives

Until recent years, precise knowledge of the **mole** was limited. It is now known that, in summer, when the young ones disperse, they first come above ground seeking new territory in which to settle down. Adult moles make short trips to the surface only rarely.

Notable for population figures that exceed those of any other species of European mammal, the **common shrew** keeps active throughout most of the day and night. Its nest, which is generally under cover in wooded areas and grasslands, is very rarely underground.

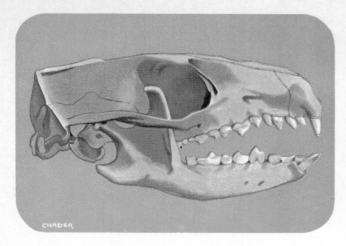 

in the Volga, Don and other rivers of southern European Russia. The feet of both are webbed, while the snout is long, tubular and mobile, and probably used for foraging under stones on the bed of the river.

Hedgehogs are highly protected by their coat of spines and their ability to roll up into a prickly ball. Consequently, they have relatively few enemies and are indifferent to danger, but suffer heavy mortality on busy highways precisely because of this. Their food is earthworms, slugs, snails, insects and some fruit and vegetable matter. The hedgehog is the only insectivore to hibernate. The principle species is the northern hedgehog, but in south-eastern Russia the long-eared hedgehog of Asia spills over into Europe. The Algerian hedgehog, typical of north-west Africa, is found on the Balearic Islands and in places on the Mediterranean coasts of Spain and France. These may have been introduced into Europe from Africa. Hedgehogs have been kept as pets at least since Roman times.

A Strange Form of Radar

THE ORDER WHICH CONTAINS the most species is the Rodentia, but bats (Chiroptera) run a close second, with thirty species. Most of these belong to the vesper bats, that is, insect-eating bats of the family Vespertilionidae. There are also five species of horseshoe bats. Two of these, the greater and the lesser horseshoe, are found throughout southern and central Europe. A third species, the Mediterranean horseshoe bat, lives in Spain, parts of France, Italy and the Balkans. A fourth, Blasius' horseshoe bat, is confined to the Dalmatian coast, Greece, northern and central Italy and Sicily. The fifth, Mehely's horseshoe bat, is found in Romania, Sardinia, Corsica, the Rhone Delta, and central Spain and Portugal.

Since bats can fly, there seems to be no reason why any of these species need be restricted in their range; yet this is the pattern for the

(top left)
A **hedgehog's skull,** like that of other typical insectivores, has a primitive shape that indicates its relationship to some of the earliest mammals known. Note the small brain case and long, extended jaws. Insectivores generally have from 44 to 48 teeth, divided into canines, incisors, premolars and molars and all very sharp-pointed; this makes them well-equipped for an insect diet.

(top right)
Hunting mainly in the water, the **Russian desman** may leave its riverbank home during warm weather to search for food under clumps of grass and piles of newly mown hay. An aquatic animal with webbed feet, it lives in the basins of the Volga, Don, and other rivers.

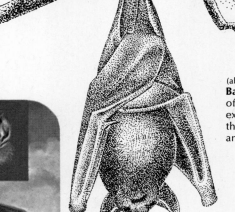

(above)
Bats' wings consist of thin membranes of skin stretched across the greatly extended digits of the front limbs. At the roost, the wings are folded up like an umbrella.

(below)
Early on summer evenings the **barbastelle** emerges from its home in hollow trees or in cracks in the walls of houses or stables to make the first of its nightly flights. Like all European bats, it hibernates for about six months of the year, spending the winter in holes, cellars and other sheltered places.

(right)
Insect-eating bats, such as this **pond bat,** find their food and avoid obstacles in flight by radar, or echo-location. They make squeaking noises and are able to detect objects by the echoes that are reflected back to their ears.

vesper bats. Some, like Daubenton's bat, the whiskered bat and the pipistrelle, or common bat, range over nearly all of Europe except for the extreme north, while most of the others have a much more limited range. An American species, the hoary bat, has turned up in the Orkneys, to the north of Scotland, on one occasion. It is remarkable that it should have come so far from its regular range.

Although the discovery was made as recently as 1940, it is now

common knowledge that insect-eating bats find their food, and also find their way about, by radar, or echo-location. A bat, when using this, squeaks and at the same time closes its ears, then immediately afterwards opens its ears to catch the echo reflected back from solid objects. It is not yet known for certain what part is played in this by the earlet, a sort of small secondary flap inside the main ear-flap. Horseshoe bats also use this sonar, but they lack an earlet. Instead, they have flaps of skin in the form of a horseshoe around the nostrils. The margins of the horseshoe are raised and lowered as the bat approaches or retreats from an object, and it is believed that the horseshoe "beams" the bat's squeaks towards an object. More than this cannot be said because there is still a difference of opinion about the function of the horseshoe.

All European bats hibernate for six months of each year. With rare exceptions they are not seen until sunset or later, and some species spend only a few hours foraging each night during spring and summer. Bat-banding has shown that these animals live twenty years or more, which is not surprising since even the most active of them spend seventy-five per cent of their time resting or sleeping.

Rabbits and Hares

Rabbits and hares used to be included among the rodents but are now classified in a separate order, the Lagomorpha. They differ from rodents in many ways, the most obvious being that they have two pairs of incisors in the upper jaw; one pair being small and functionless and lying behind the functional pair. Another feature of the lagomorphs is that they have enamel on the backs of the incisors, whereas rodents have it only on the front. The teeth of rabbits and hares are, therefore, less effectively self-sharpening than those of rodents, and their use is limited to chewing fibrous vegetation.

The best-known lagomorph is the rabbit or coney, if only because it

(top left)
Included in the family of rabbits and hares, the **pika** is about the size of a guinea pig and has very short ears. It is found only in rocky, mountainous areas. Like its long-eared relatives, its diet consists mostly of fibrous vegetation.

(top right)
An inhabitant of dense woods, particularly pine forests, the **red squirrel** builds its nest in the fork of a tree and remains active throughout the year. Its diet, like that of other squirrels, is made up of nuts, seeds, buds, and so forth, with some insects and, occasionally, nestling birds and eggs.

has been spread so disastrously beyond its original home. Whether it originally came from Spain or central Europe is not known. Nor can we be certain whether the rabbit spread naturally across Europe or if it was carried by the Romans. The rabbit was unknown in Britain until the Norman Conquest in the eleventh century. Since then it has been introduced into the Canary Islands and Madeira, the Ukraine and Australia, where it became a serious pest. Today its members have been reduced by the spread of myxomatosis, a disease of mucoid degeneration.

Rabbits are gregarious and live in burrows they themselves excavate. A collection of burrows should strictly be called a bury, but it is more usual to call it a warren, although a warren was originally an enclosure for semi-domesticated rabbits.

Rabbits differ in outward appearance from hares but they differ much more in habits, especially in their breeding habits. The doe rabbit usually digs a nursery burrow, known as a stop, away from the bury, where the bucks will not molest her offspring. The stop is a blind burrow sloping gently to a chamber a few inches below the surface, which the doe lines with fur from her own breast. The young are born blind, deaf, helpless and naked. The doe visits them once a day to suckle them and seals the entrance to the stop with earth when she leaves. The young are weaned at three weeks.

Apart from its larger size the brown hare of the lowlands has longer hind legs proportionately, therefore is swifter and covers more ground, and it has black-tipped ears. More solitary also, the brown hare's development is markedly different. The young, or leverets, are born fully haired, with eyes and ears open, on the surface of the ground in a form, which is no more than a depression in a tussock of grass, where the doe visits to suckle them.

The arctic hare lives on the tundra and taiga of the north, with isolated populations on mountains in the Alps, Scotland, Ireland and on some Baltic islands. These isolated populations have been given various names, such as mountain hare, variable and blue hare, springing from their change from a brown summer coat to a white winter coat.

Squirrels

THE ORDER RODENTIA has many representatives in Europe. Most familiar are rats and mice; but squirrels, marmots, porcupines and beavers are other members of the order. The European red squirrel has the usual form of tree-dwelling squirrels, with a well-developed bushy tail. It inhabits especially pine forests, building a nest in the fork of a tree which it occupies throughout the year, and does not hibernate. The red squirrel's food is much the same as that of other squirrels: nuts, beech mast, pine seeds, green buds, fungi, some insects, nestling birds and eggs, except that it takes a higher proportion of pine seeds. Its main enemies are the pine and beech martens and the eagle owl.

(below)
Squirrels have many natural enemies and often need to move their young to a fresh nest. The mother squirrel carries her babies by holding them in her teeth.

(bottom)
Larger and stronger than the red squirrel, the **grey squirrel** has replaced it in some areas, especially where the red squirrel has been reduced in number by disease.

Marmots live in burrows high in the mountains. Although they hibernate in winter, their sleep is not continuous. They awake occasionally to eat their stored foods.

When tree squirrels leap into the air, the body becomes flattened, the legs are spread-eagled and the tail acts as a rudder. The **flying squirrel** has a web of skin along both flanks that functions as a parachute.

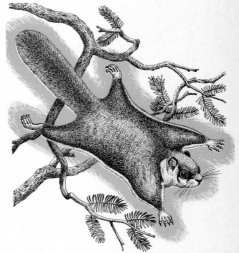

Europe has relatively few squirrels; in addition to the red squirrel, there is one flying squirrel found mainly in Finland and only two ground squirrels, both confined to eastern Europe. The flying squirrel is similar to the introduced gray squirrel but only about half its size, and it has a gliding membrane along each flank. The common ground squirrel, or souslik, about eight inches long with a short tail and its back buff mottled with dark brown, lives in burrows. It feeds mainly on the ground, especially on cereals, on green food and some insects, carrying much food away in cheek pouches to store in its burrow. In winter it hibernates. The spotted ground squirrel, slightly smaller, its back a dark brown profusely spotted with white, has very similar habits, and like the common ground squirrel is a pest to agriculture.

A marmot is merely a large ground squirrel, with much the same habits. The alpine marmot of Europe lives in the Alps and the Carpathians, on the pastures above the tree line. Its nest, of dry grass, is several feet below ground, and here a whole family of marmots may sleep the winter through, from October to April, with the mouth of the burrow sealed. During the summer marmots feed on grasses and herbaceous plants, using a warning whistle at the approach of danger to send all the marmots scuttling to safety. Their enemies are few, however, high up in the mountains, as reflected by their rate of reproduction. A single pair may have one litter of two to four young once a year, sometimes once in two years, which is a low rate of multiplication for a rodent.

There used to be a steppe marmot on the plains of Hungary. This species is still found in Asia, but appears to have been eliminated from Europe by the conversion of virgin steppe grassland to arable land.

The Beaver and the Porcupine

THE BEAVER, ANOTHER LARGE RODENT, was formerly as plentiful across Europe as it used to be in North America. The European species differs from its relative in North America in small details only. It was wiped out in Britain by the thirteenth century, but in western

A large ground squirrel, the **alpine marmot** lives in pastures above the tree line, where it has few enemies. It may be seen on warm summer days, sitting upright on its hind legs.

(opposite page, top left)
Though imported into Europe to be farmed for its fur, the South American **coypu,** or **nutria,** escaped from the fur farms and settled in swamps and along waterways in various parts of Europe.

Europe there are remnant colonies in the Rhone, in France, and in the Elbe, in Germany. Its numbers were severely reduced in European Russia, also, but in modern times reintroduction has gone some way in restoring them.

Another large rodent, the crested porcupine, is found today in Italy, including Sicily, as well as in Albania and parts of Yugoslavia. This species is also found throughout Africa and into southern Asia. It is known to have been introduced into Albania and Yugoslavia. Whether its occurrence in Italy and Sicily is also the result of a much earlier introduction is unknown. It may well be; just as the South American coypu, brought to Europe to be bred in captivity for its fur, has escaped and become established along waterways in England, Holland, France, Denmark, Germany and parts of eastern Europe. In the U.S.S.R. the coypu has been deliberately liberated, to be harvested for its fur.

The "Mouse" Family

ALTHOUGH THE NAME OF THE NEXT FAMILY of rodents bears the suffix "mouse" its bearers are not very closely related to true mice. They are the five species of dormice, animals made famous by the character at the tea party in *Alice in Wonderland* that appeared to be in a state of perpetual somnolence. This does, to a large extent, represent its true character. The dormouse normally sleeps throughout the daylight hours and hibernates from October to April. This applies more especially to the hazel dormouse, but is true to a greater or lesser degree of the fat or edible dormouse, the garden dormouse, the forest dormouse and the mouse-tailed dormouse. All are small rodents with a soft fur and hairy or semi-bushy tails, except for the mouse-tailed dormouse. They live in low bushes or trees, feeding on nuts, fruit, seeds, insects and birds' eggs, but the diet is more vegetarian in some species than others.

The hazel dormouse is three and one-half inches long with a tail of nearly the same length. In summer it rests by day in a nest in bushes, especially hazel, made of honeysuckle bark, and comes out at night to

(right)
Here we see the **coypu** showing off its four enormous, bevelled incisors, two above and two below, an arrangement characteristic of all rodents.

(far right)
A few centuries ago, the European **beaver** was as common throughout Europe as the related American species once was in North America. This flat-tailed, web-footed animal has been almost completely exterminated except in a few rivers, mainly in Western Europe.

feed. Its winter nests are at ground level or below ground. It suffers little from predators in summer but shows an eighty per cent mortality during the hibernation period.

The edible dormouse, seven inches long with a bushy tail of nearly the same length, is more squirrel-like. Grey in tone, it lives mostly in mature woodland, and its diet includes bark, which makes it a pest in plantations and orchards. Its nest is made in a fork of a tree or in a hollow tree; its winter nests are at ground level between buttress roots.

The garden dormouse and the forest dormouse are intermediate in size between these two. The mouse-tailed dormouse, found in one locality in south-eastern Europe, was unknown until 1924.

The mole rat, confined to south-eastern Europe, is also found in south-western Asia and in North Africa. It is a mole-shaped rodent highly adapted for burrowing. The entire head is used in burrowing. It is wedge-shaped and flattened, and has a line of stiff hairs on either side, from the muzzle to the vestigial ear. This extends the surface of the head which is used as a shovel for moving soil loosened by the claws

(top right)
After hibernating from October till April, the **hazel dormouse** continues to rest by day in its nest, which is usually made of honeysuckle bark. It comes out only at night to search for nuts, fruits, seeds and eggs.

(above, left)
The **edible dormouse,** with its bushy tail, looks like a squirrel, but it may be distinguished from the latter by its bulging eyes and smaller size.

(above, right)
Like the other dormice, the **garden dormouse** often lives in old nests of birds or squirrels. It is commonly found in gardens and orchards, where it lives more on the ground than most of the other members of its family.

Active day and night, families of **shrews** sometimes move in "caravans," each animal following closely behind the one in front of it, with the mother leading the way.

Wherever man lives, the **house mouse** will also be found dwelling, though this small rodent can live equally well in fields and in open woods. It is a prolific breeder, and any attempt by man to reduce its numbers is bound to be futile.

and the powerful incisors. The mole rat has a coat of short hair, is tailless, and its eyes are covered with skin. It feeds largely on roots and bulbs.

The birch mouse and the steppe mouse of eastern Europe are related to the bipedal jerboas but they do not jump. They have more the habits of dormice except in feeding, their diet consisting mainly of insects found in rotten wood or under bark. They are mouselike, with all four legs about the same length, but with very long tails.

The True Mice

IT IS IRONIC that the two kinds of small rodents most well-known in Western Europe, the mouse and the rat, which have lent their names and set our standards in western Europe for all small rodents should, in fact, be alien intruders into the European fauna. The order Rodentia is the largest order among mammals, with some 350 genera and nearly 7,000 species or subspecies. And the largest family in this large order is the Muridae, which includes rats, mice and voles.

The Muridae is subdivided into three subfamilies: the Murinae; the Old World rats and mice, the Cricetinae or hamsters; and the Microtinae, the voles and lemmings as well as the mice and rats of the New World.

Although in outward appearance there is often nothing to distinguish the New World rats and mice from their relatives in the Old World, the pattern of their cheek-teeth is an infallible key to their identity. Both groups have the same number of teeth, and these teeth have the same general proportions and arrangement and serve the same purposes. But the cheek-teeth of the New World rats and mice have only two longitudinal rows of cusps or tubercles, while the Old World rats and mice always have three. A good example of the parallelism in outward appearance is found in the white-footed mice, or deer mice, the best-known and most numerous of the Microtinae in North America, and the long-tailed field mice, the most numerous of the Murinae in Europe. The two also agree very closely in habits.

The long-tailed field mouse, also known as the wood mouse, is about the size of a house mouse but has a longer tail. It is a "pretty" mouse, with pure white feet and underparts, large limpid eyes and large ears, and it lacks the unpleasant scent associated with "ordinary" mice. Another feature which distinguishes it at once from the house mouse is its jumping and climbing ability. It often progresses by bounds, and although all four feet touch the ground together, it looks like a miniature kangaroo. The female with young will run and jump, with two of them each firmly holding a teat. Longtails will also climb bushes and trees.

The longtail is the most numerous and widespread of Europe's mammals, and can be found everywhere except in the extreme north. It inhabits every kind of country, from woods and fields to gardens, some-

Harvest mice are adept climbers. Not only can they grasp the stems of plants with both front and hind paws, but the tail is prehensile and can be wrapped around a stem to assist the animal in climbing. It is, in effect, a fifth hand.

times entering houses. Its food consists of grain, nuts, berries and fruit, as well as succulent vegetables and some insects. A nocturnal animal, it tends to remain under cover during the day, under leaf litter or piles of brushwood or in subterranean burrows. It will hoard food, sometimes using a deserted bird's nest in a bush or tree for this purpose. Almost every mammalian predator, especially owls and other birds, weasels, stoats and cats, preys upon it.

The longtail breeds throughout the summer, and all the year round in southern Europe. Litters of four to six young are produced monthly, and the young reach breeding maturity in under two months. Its average life span is less than six months, but it may live for up to two years.

A close relative of the longtail is the yellow-necked mouse, which resembles it so closely that the two are often confused. The yellow-neck has a yellow or chestnut patch on the throat and chest, is more robust and vigorous and a better jumper and climber than its cousin and more often comes into houses for the winter. It has a more localized distribution, and in places has been known to interbreed with the longtail. This may have been responsible for some stories of haunted houses, for when bounding over the floor on a still night in winter it sounds like heavy human footsteps.

The smallest relative of the longtail is without a common name, since it was unknown until 1952. *Apodemus microps* is smaller than the longtail and inhabits the grasslands of Czechoslovakia, Hungary and the Ukraine. The largest relative, the rock mouse, lives on rocky hillsides in Dalmatia, Albania and Greece. Another relative, larger than the longtail, is the striped mouse of central and south-west Europe. It has a black stripe along the mid-line of the back, and is commonly seen on agricultural land.

The smallest European rodent is the harvest mouse. Four inches long, nearly half of which is tail, the harvest mouse lives in what has been called the stalk zone, climbing among the taller herbaceous plants and tall grasses and feeding on seeds. It took naturally, therefore, to living among cereal crops such as wheat and oats. When pregnant the female shreds grass leaves to construct a ball-shaped nest slung between two or three tall stems. In it litters of from four to six are produced between April and September.

The climbing prowess of a harvest mouse is due to its ability to grasp stems with both front and hind paws and to wrap its tail around them. Each twenty-four hours is spent in alternating spells of from three to four hours of resting and feeding. The mouse sleeps in nests of shredded grass at ground level.

The house mouse needs no introduction to most people no matter which country it lives in. Although there is no documentation of its early spread, this mouse is commonly believed to have originated in Central Asia and to have spread thence, aided no doubt, as were the black and brown rats, by making man its unwilling ally, sheltering in

Common shrews have at least three litters of six to seven young each year. Their maximum span of life is one year, the adults dying in the autumn and their young ones dying by the following autumn, provided they have not succumbed to natural hazards before then.

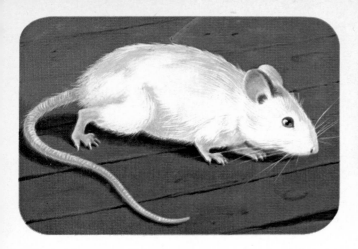

his buildings and feeding on his food stores. The house mouse was known to the ancient Greeks, and presumably had overrun Europe by their time or soon after. Since then it has been carried around the world in ships, even as far as arctic islands.

Although this represents the customary view, a more modern idea is that certain subspecies of the mouse living in south-east and southern Europe may be indigenous; these subspecies live in the open country-side away from man's own dwellings. This can, however, hardly be more than an opinion, since wherever the house mouse occurs there are also groups of individuals that live in grassland or among coarse vegetation. It is a general symptom of the adaptability of rodents that while some species have a tendency to batten on man they can just as readily live off the land. The adaptability of the house mouse is further emphasized by the colonies living permanently in refrigerated meat stores, growing longer coats against the cold and nesting in the frozen carcasses.

House mice usually breed throughout the year, producing ten litters a year of from four to seven young per litter. The young become sexually mature at six weeks.

The Rat

THERE IS MORE CERTAINTY about the origin of the two species of rat. The black rat came from South-east Asia and in the Middle Ages was responsible for the Black Death which ravaged western Europe, killing thirty per cent or more of the population. The Black Death, or bubonic plague, was carried by the rat flea. The rat appears to have been unknown in Europe before the time of the Crusades to the Holy Land and it is said to have been brought from there in the twelfth century in the returning Crusaders' ships.

The brown rat from Central Asia followed several centuries later. It is also known in Great Britain as the Norway or Norwegian rat, be-

(top left)
Bred in captivity, the common mouse quickly turns albino, and the red-eyed **white mouse** type is maintained for many generations. This lack of pigmentation may affect part or all of the body, particularly the skin.

(top right)
Rodents, such as the **black rat,** have highly developed incisors. The black rat feeds on anything and lives anywhere, though in Europe it is chiefly a parasite of man and is not so frequently found in the wild state as is the brown rat.

The **crested porcupine**, though more common in Africa, is found wild in a few parts of Mediterranean Europe. There is a strong suspicion that it was introduced into Southern Europe a long time ago, but this cannot now be proven.

Although some people still confuse the **hedgehog** with the porcupine, the two belong to different orders. The porcupine is a large rodent and the hedgehog is an insectivore. Despite its place in the most primitive order of mammals, however, the hedgehog eats more earthworms, slugs and snails than it does insects.

cause it first reached the British Isles in ships coming from Norway, and as the Hanoverian rat, because it arrived in the eighteenth century at the time the Hanoverian kings were on the throne of England.

The names "black" and "brown" are misleading because both species vary in hue. The typical form of the black rat is blackish above and sooty on the underparts, but the more numerous variety, the Alexandrian rat, is brown above and dingy white underneath, almost exactly as in the brown rat; while the roof or tree rat of the Mediterranean region and other warmer parts of Europe is reddish brown on the back and white or lemon underneath. Conversely, a black variety of the brown or Norway rat is not uncommon. The two species can be most reliably distinguished by their build; the black rat is of a lighter build and has longer ears than the brown rat, and its tail is longer than the head and body combined.

The black rat has never established itself in the cold parts of the world, being of a more southerly origin than the brown rat, but over the warmer parts of the world it is found wherever man is living. It is more of a climber than the brown rat, going higher in buildings and even making use of overhead cables to climb from one building to another. The rat-proofing of the lower parts of large buildings, especially warehouses, has been to the disadvantage of the black rat. This, along with the heavier build and greater aggressiveness of the brown rat, has caused the black rat to be largely absent except in seaport areas. The black rat is, however, found more commonly on ships, and is often referred to as the ships' rat.

Both species of rat have become spread over the world, but the brown rat has had greater success and is now found in most of the world's populated regions. The brown rat will make itself at home wherever cover is available, whether natural or artificial. If sufficient food is available it will settle down equally well on arable land, in hedgerows, woods, haystacks or sewers. Besides causing enormous damage to food-stocks, the brown rat also carries infected fleas. The only good that can be said of it is that a domestic form of the brown rat, the white or pied tame rat, is used frequently in laboratory experiments and as a pet.

The black rat is prolific but the brown rat is even more so. A single female may have five to six litters a year, with an average of eight young to a litter, but where food is abundant litters of seventeen, nineteen and even twenty-three have been recorded.

Another member of the subfamily Murinae has been spread by ships, but to a limited extent. This is the spiny mouse of the northern half of Africa and of south-west Asia. It has reached Cyprus and Crete, thereby obtaining a toehold in Europe. It feeds more on insects than most mice, is solitary and a slow breeder, and therefore unlikely to become a pest.

The Hamster

THE HAMSTERS (subfamily Cricetinae) include three species: the common hamster, the Romanian hamster and the grey hamster. The Romanian hamster is similar to the golden hamster, the domesticated form from Syria. Like the grey hamster, it is found only in eastern and south-eastern Europe. The highly aggressive common hamster is larger, about the size of a guinea pig, but with a short tail.

In its habits the common hamster resembles a ground squirrel, digging underground burrows and hoarding food, the collection of which is aided, as in the pet golden hamster, by cheek pouches for carrying away surplus food. The common hamster hibernates, but somewhat intermittently, from October to March. During this time it wakes at frequent intervals and feeds from its hoard. The common hamster is peculiar in having the fur of its underparts darker than that on the back.

Lemmings and Voles

THE NEXT SUBFAMILY OF RODENTS, the Microtinae, includes two species of lemmings and fourteen species of voles. Lemmings, voles and hamsters differ from Old World rats and mice in having a blunter muzzle, small eyes and small ears largely hidden in the fur.

There are few animals about which there has been a more persist-

Voles are blunt-nosed rodents with the peculiarity of a cyclic rise and fall in their populations. Occasionally the **meadow vole** can become so numerous that the grasslands seem to be moving with them. At such times the grass is eaten down to the ground.

ent and dramatic story than the Norwegian lemming and its mass migrations into the sea and to certain death. To understand the true story of the lemming it is necessary to know that certain members of the Microtinae are subject to periodic or cyclic rises and falls in population. In all species of animals there are fluctuations in numbers, but these are more marked than usual in lemmings and in some voles, and they occur in cycles of from four to ten years. The natural home of the Norwegian lemming is in the mountains, where it feeds on grass and other plants. Regular rises in population take place about every four years. Sometimes, for reasons not yet wholly clear, the rises are excessive and the surplus population spills over into the valleys where the lemmings seek new territories. Those unsuccessful in finding new homes must go farther afield. These wanderers tend to become channelled by the lie of the land, but there is no directional migration and no organized columns of the travellers. Lemmings coming to a river bank will swim across, but quickly become drowned if the water is anything but calm. Some reach the fiords and, seeing land beyond, try to cross and are drowned, sometimes in huge numbers, and it is these occasions that have given rise to the fantastic stories of their strange activity.

The rate of breeding of lemmings is quite variable, which is one of the factors in the cyclic rises. The normal rate is two litters a year of from four to eight young, which come into breeding condition at about two months. When a population reaches a peak, overcrowding causes a drop in the reproductive rate, and an increase in the number of predators, due to the greater number of lemmings to feed upon, also helps to cause a crash in lemming numbers.

The Norwegian lemming is also found on the tundra of northern Europe. There is a second species, the wood lemming, about which little is known except that it occurs in parts of central Sweden and Finland and feeds exclusively on mosses.

The first of the fourteen species of vole is the bank vole, about four inches long with a two-inch tail, mouselike but with the blunt muzzle and small eyes and ears typical of Microtinae. It is found especially in deciduous woodlands and where there are bushes or hedges. Active by day, it feeds on seeds, buds and insects. Sometimes it also climbs into the bushes and eats bark, roots and bulbs.

The northern red-backed vole is very similar, but often enters houses in winter. It lives in the extreme north of Scandinavia and Finland, and ranges across northern Asia. It is interesting that this vole is probably of the same species as the red-backed mouse of Canada and the northern United States. The grey-backed vole lives above the birch-line in Scandinavia and Finland and is more nearly related to the bank vole.

The water vole, often misnamed the water rat, is the largest vole native to Europe. It is eight inches long in the head and body, with a five-inch tail, dark brown fur and the usual blunt muzzle, small eyes

The **garden dormouse** may get into houses, since it seeks out human-inhabited areas. It feeds on fruit, grain and even eggs.

Wolves were formerly very common throughout Europe, but their attacks on domestic stock—after the vanishing of the aurochs and the bison, their natural prey—brought rigorous persecution. They are now found only in the wilder parts of Western Europe, occasionally coming down from the forested hills during severe winters to raid domestic stocks.

and small ears. In Britain it keeps close to water, burrowing in the banks and swimming across rivers to feed on water plants or water snails. In the north and east of continental Europe the same form is more terrestrial, and consequently is given the specific name *terrestris*, whereas in Britain it is called *amphibius*. In Spain and south-west France another form, *sapidus*, can be identified, and in central Europe another form is known as *scherman*. The appearance and habits of all of them are substantially similar. Moreover, opinions among zoologists differ on whether we should recognize in these four forms two species or four, but they can all be separated by chromosome counts.

This division into genetic groups, whether species or subspecies, families or merely forms, becomes apparent when we come to the field vole. It is a brown animal, the shade varying from yellowish brown to reddish brown, and is four inches long with a tail of one and one-half inches. Almost every large island or group of islands around Scotland has its subspecies of field vole. In continental Europe the field vole has a similar range to that of the bank vole, except that it extends farther south. There is also the Mediterranean vole, the northern vole and the alpine vole, each differing in its range, habits and appearance.

The study of these small mouselike voles, as well as of the several species of root voles, is a matter for the specialist. All that need be noted here is that the field vole is subject to similar rises and falls in numbers to those seen in lemmings. As a consequence there occur "plague years", when the populations build up to such proportions that the grasslands seem alive with voles, and these are followed by a "crash", when the numbers fall steeply.

Wolves, Jackals and Foxes

THE POPULATION OF RODENTS is largely kept in check by the carnivores, the flesh-eaters. In Europe these fall largely into three families: the Canidae, of which foxes, wolves and jackals are representatives, the Mustelidae or weasel family, and the Felidae, which includes the lynx and the wild cat. Other members of the Carnivora are the brown bear and, in arctic Europe, the polar bear.

The European wolf belongs to the same species as the Asiatic wolf and the North American gray or timber wolf. Yellowish or brownish gray brindled with black, with a drooping tail, it is about four and one-half feet in length with a tail sixteen inches long. It weighs about 110 pounds. There are five to nine young in a litter born in dens among rocks, in thick cover or in burrows either freshly made or taken over from other animals. The pack is usually a family party of parents and the young of the year, but sometimes with the young of the previous year also. Wolves traverse a large territory; they may kill at one place and be forty miles away the next day, possibly not returning to the original spot for weeks. In Europe they must subsist on small game or on domestic stock, which, along with their wide-ranging habits, has brought about their elimination in many parts of Europe.

The Indian jackal is native to southern Asia, but also extends into Asia Minor and the northern half of Africa. A form of this species also occurs in Hungary and the Balkans. Smaller than the wolf, it is very similar in many ways, but lives in more wooded countries, keeps nearer to human habitations and feeds on small mammals, birds, eggs, fish and carrion.

Foxes are represented in Europe by the red fox and the arctic fox. The red fox extends across Europe and Asia, and some authorities regard the red fox of North America as belonging to the same species. Its coat is variable in hue, with frequent mutations, especially in North America; among these are the cross fox, which is red with a black band

(below)
The plaintive howl of the **jackal** may be heard over great distances at night, especially in Hungary, Greece and surrounding areas of Southern Europe. This animal is fond of eating carrion, but it also occasionally attacks poultry and other farmyard animals.

(right)
The wild horse of Europe became extinct during the middle of the last century. There are, however, a number of strains of horses that have escaped and gone wild, and one of the more famous of these is the **New Forest pony.**

across the shoulders, and the silver fox—a lustrous black with white tips on many of the guard hairs.

The red fox is typically two feet in length, with a tail or brush a little over a foot long. The coat is reddish with a white front, and the ears and tail are tipped with black, sometimes white on the tail. The fox is nocturnal, hunting at night for rats, mice, voles, ground-nesting birds and their eggs, frogs, insects and rabbits. It also eats grass and berries in season. The cubs, born in spring, have a woolly brown coat, number three to eight in a litter and reach sexual maturity in eighteen months.

The arctic or white fox ranges the arctic islands and coasts of Europe, Asia and North America. In summer it haunts the rocky coasts feeding largely on ground-nesting birds and their eggs, as well as on stranded fish and other carrion. It does not hibernate, but feeds in winter on quantities of lemmings which it stores in crevices for the purpose. It also eats the remains of seals killed and left by polar bears.

Slightly smaller than the red fox, the arctic fox has a shorter muzzle and small rounded ears. It is brown in summer but moults to white for the winter. One phase of this change, known as the blue fox, is farmed for its pelt.

The Bear

THE EUROPEAN BROWN BEAR averages six feet in length and 450 to 550 pounds according to the season, but skins of much larger specimens are preserved in museums in the U.S.S.R. The brown bear is now rare in most parts of Europe but a few are still to be found in the Pyrenees, the Carpathians and the Alps, in Italy, Scandinavia and the Balkans and more extensively in eastern Europe. The body is heavy, with practically no tail; the feet are broad and flattened, with five toes on each foot bearing stout non-retractile claws. Brown bears feed on wild fruits, honey, insects and other small creatures, a variety of vegetable matter, fish when available, and any flesh food they come across. They have been known to kill large animals, even domestic stock. Although bears have poor sight, their sense of smell and hearing are acute. Two young are normally delivered at a birth while the mother is in "hibernation", that is, denned up for the winter after accumulating fat during the autumn. The newborn young are small and helpless.

The polar bear is one of the largest and certainly the most carnivorous of the bear family, as it needs to be, living in the Arctic where vegetation is almost non-existent. Its length is seven to eight feet, and large specimens reaching as much as nine feet are sometimes found. The average weight for a male is 900 pounds, for a female 700, but the maximum for a well-grown male is 1,600 pounds. The long head, "roman" nose, long neck, powerful limbs and broad feet with hairy soles enabling it to move freely over the ice are all characteristic features, as is the habit of swinging the head from side to side as if continually searching for or smelling out food. Seals, the favourite prey, are stalked by taking advantage of the cover afforded by hummocks of snow. A seal sleeping at the edge of the ice may be approached by water. A dead whale may attract polar bears from miles around; the animals leave the land and travel on drifting ice, if need be, to follow a supply of food. Polar bears are expert at diving and swimming, and have often been seen swimming strongly miles from land. They do not hibernate, and the two young are born in the depth of the polar winter, in a hole deep in the snow.

Polar bears appear to have no instinctive fear of man, and, impelled either by hunger or curiosity, they will visit human camps or ice-bound ships, and they will open up and destroy explorers' food caches even when protected under heavy stones. They were formerly hunted by the Eskimos with dogs and lances, and against these proved themselves formidable adversaries, but they have little chance against firearms.

(below)
Lithe and agile, **Weasels** are lightning-quick in seizing their prey. Their small size enables them to follow mice into their burrows. There is an old saying that a weasel can pass through a wedding ring.

(below)
Somewhat larger than the weasel but similar in habit and appearance is the **stoat.** Northern stoats turn white in winter except for the black tip of the tail. The white pelt is known as **ermine.**

(right)
Although there is a native species in Europe, the North American **mink** was introduced for fur farming. Some of these animals escaped and established breeding colonies in the wild. With no natural enemies, there is a possibility that they may become troublesome around fisheries and poultry farms.

Weasels, Martens and Mink

T<small>HE</small> M<small>USTELIDAE OR WEASEL FAMILY</small> includes the weasel, stoat, marten, wolverine, badger and otter. Weasels are the smallest of carnivores, the male of the common weasel of Europe being eight and one-half inches long with a tail of two and three-quarter inches. The female is a good deal smaller, and in some parts of England the term "cane weasel" is used for the females because they appear to represent a distinct species. The least weasel is smaller still, the male being nine inches in total length. Although it is not found in the British Isles, it extends from western Europe to eastern Asia and also occurs in North America.

In the colder latitudes, weasels turn white in winter even to the tip of the tail, and this gives us a ready means of distinction from the next largest member of the weasel family in Europe, the stoat or ermine. These animals also range across Europe and northern Asia, as well as North America. They are small, reddish brown animals with a black tip to the tail, and in those latitudes in which the stoat turns white in winter the tail tip remains black. It is in this condition that the pelt is known as ermine, traditionally reserved for people of noble rank. The male stoat is a foot long with a tail of four inches but the female is smaller. All stoats hunt their prey by scent, tirelessly and persistently following the trail like miniature bloodhounds, killing by a bite at the base of the skull and frequently eating the brain first. They usually hunt singly but the young, six to ten in number, follow their mother when old enough, giving rise to stories of stoats hunting in packs.

Under stress of excitement a stoat discharges a thick, foul-smelling yellowish liquid from its anal glands. Its larger relative, the polecat, has this characteristic to a greater degree, and in former times was known as the "foul marten". The polecat's normal diet consists of voles and rabbits, but it will readily turn to poultry, and for this reason has been persecuted throughout its range. The adult male polecat is up to one

(top left)
Found nearly everywhere in Europe, the **polecat,** a medium-sized member of the weasel family, has a bad reputation as a killer of poultry. Consequently, it has been widely persecuted, except in the wilder parts of its range.

(top right)
Somewhat awkward in the trees, the **beech marten** was originally found mainly in rocky areas: hence its alternate name, "stone marten." Nowadays it may often be seen near houses and in towns on the margins of forests. Unafraid of man, it hides in deserted buildings or in piles of wood or stones and does its hunting by night.

Like the North American skunk, the **polecat** gives off an extremely offensive odor whenever it is frightened or excited; this accounts for the name given it in former times: the "foul marten."

and one-half feet long with a tail eight inches long. Its fur is long, with a creamy-buff underfur and long black guard hairs. This animal is terrestrial, unlike its close relative the pine marten. The pine marten also differs from the polecat in its lack of offensive scent, and is sometimes spoken of as the "sweet marten". It is two and one-half feet long, with a dark rich brown fur and yellow throat. It nests in hollow trees, produces three or four young at a time and normally feeds on squirrels. The pine marten has been rigorously hunted in the past, both for the value of its pelt and because it made excellent sport for the common people who were barred from such activities as deer hunting. The beech marten is closely related, occupying southern Europe and extending northwards to overlap the range of the pine marten. Its alternative name is "stone marten", but beech marten is more descriptive because it occupies the deciduous woodland zones. Although it climbs well, it does not possess the pine marten's skill among the trees, and tends to live more on the rocky hillsides.

The European mink is closely related to the American mink in appearance and habits, and both are just over two feet long, eight inches of which is tail. The mink is highly aquatic and an excellent swimmer. It tends to keep to wooded waterways and marshlands but will hunt at considerable distance from water if need be.

Wolverines, Badgers and Otters

THE LARGEST OF THE WEASEL FAMILY is the wolverine of the arctic and sub-arctic regions of Europe, Asia and North America. It is thick-bodied and short-legged, with a shaggy coat, and is four feet long including a one-foot-long tail. The thick, loose fur is very dark brown, with a pale brown band on the sides. Weighing up to thirty-six pounds, it fears nothing. The wolverines will occasionally attack large game such as deer, and is credited with great cunning in robbing traps and hunters' caches in the Far North.

The badger is also a member of the weasel family although it lacks the long slender body, and the scent from the anal glands is inoffensive —rather sweet and musty. The European badger, which has close relatives ranging across north Asia to China and Japan, is noted for its strength and fearlessness. About three feet long with a seven inch tail, its body is a grizzled grey, the legs and undersides blackish, and it has a very striking black-and-white-striped head. Its nocturnal habits and native caution enable it to live in a locality without attracting much notice. The boar badger may weigh up to twenty-five pounds, the sow up to twenty-two pounds. Its loose hide makes it difficult for dogs to get an effective grip, and its powerful jaws can inflict severe damage on an attacker. The ancient sport of badger baiting was a recognition of the animal's ability to defend itself effectively. A badger's preferred food is young rabbits, which it detects by scent and digs out of their nesting chamber, but it also eats beetles, earthworms, insect grubs and even carrion, besides bulbs, fruit, grain and nuts. The European badger does not hibernate and three to five young are born in the spring.

Badgers live in labyrinthine systems of burrows, which sometimes involve areas of several hundred yards and which have evidently been used by communities of badgers for centuries.

The European otter is very similar in appearance and habits to otters found in Asia, North and South America and Africa, the main difference being in their size. They hunt in rivers and lakes, using holes in the bank, often under the roots of a tree, for resting and for the birth of their young. The European otter attains a head-and-body length of two and one-half feet, with a tail one and one-half feet. The males, or "dogs", weigh twenty to twenty-five pounds, the females, or "bitches",

(above)
Largest member of the weasel family, the **wolverine** is credited with a voracious appetite. This animal is sometimes called the "glutton" because of the way it robs hunters' traps and raids their food stores, for almost anything that is edible is a likely meal for the wolverine.

(left)
The eyes of the **genet** have vertically-slit pupils like those of a cat. This animal, which looks like a cross between a cat and a mongoose, is believed to have been introduced from Africa.

(right)
The original European **fallow deer** became extinct many centuries ago, and its bones are found only in ancient refuse heaps. The fallow deer now running wild in Europe belongs to an Asiatic species.

(below)
Mouflon, or **wild sheep,** live in small groups on rugged, mountainous terrain. Although considerably reduced in number over the years, they have been reintroduced in various mountain areas of Central Europe.

fifteen to eighteen pounds. The ears are small and, like the nostrils, can be closed under water. The fur is thick and close, and was at one time regarded as quite valuable. The feet are well webbed, and the animal is an expert swimmer and diver. The claws are small.

All otters are extremely playful. Taken young—two to four are born in spring—they make delightful pets, and in the wild state the adults are particularly fond of sliding. Often a clay bank is worn smooth where a particular place is used as a slide, and in winter snowy banks are commonly used for this sport. Otters are often persecuted by fishermen because they are thought to destroy fish, although the fish they take are mainly diseased. They are seldom seen by day. Frequently they desert the rivers to live along the rocky seacoasts, but they are not to be confused with sea otters, which are different animals.

The Egyptian mongoose, a native of northern Africa, is also found in Spain, Italy and Yugoslavia, but there is good reason for believing that it was introduced to these areas. The feline genet, another African species, one that looks like a cross between a mongoose and a tabby cat, is also found in Portugal, Spain and western France. There is a strong possibility that it is also present in Europe as a result of introduction.

The Cat Family

THE POWERFULLY BUILT EUROPEAN WILDCAT preys upon a variety of animals and birds. Formerly abundant throughout Europe and the British Isles (except Ireland), they are now much reduced in numbers due to clearing of forests and settlement of the land. The wildcat weighs between ten and fifteen pounds. It is about two feet long, and the blunt-tipped tail adds an additional twelve inches. In appearance it is

not unlike a large heavily-built striped tabby cat. In Scotland the wildcat lives in rocky places and usually has a safe retreat among rocks, where from two to fifteen kittens are born. Its food consists mainly of hare, rabbit and grouse. In deer forests its presence is welcomed as a means of keeping down hares, which may spoil a deer-stalker's approach. In the new forest plantations it is encouraged as a check on rabbits which might destroy the young trees; but elsewhere it is persecuted.

The lynx, a similar-sized member of the cat family, used to range throughout Europe as far south as the Mediterranean but has been exterminated in western Europe except for Scandinavia and Spain. Its main strongholds are now in the Balkans and in the forests of eastern Europe. Like the wildcat, the lynx is solitary and nocturnal, but it keeps more to the ground.

The Hoofed Animals

THE LAST GROUP OF ANIMALS we shall deal with are the hoofed animals, which have had a more varied history in Europe than in any other part of the world. There used to be twelve species of hoofed animals including the aurochs and the tarpan, or wild horse; in spite of a severe reduction in their numbers there are now seventeen species, seven of which have been introduced from other parts of the world. The axis deer from southern Asia and the Japanese sika deer are now feral in many places, and the Chinese muntjac and the Chinese water deer are also feral; the North American white-tailed deer has been introduced, and the musk-ox of North America has become feral in parts of Norway. The fallow deer that was originally native in Europe has been wiped out, and the present-day fallow has been introduced from south-west Asia. From parks on large estates, many escaped and went wild. The reindeer is now almost wholly domesticated in Europe, and all the rest of the deer family are greatly reduced in numbers, some of them only surviving as the result of stringent protection. The European bison, or wisent, is preserved in the Bialowieza Forest in Poland. Until the Middle Ages it ranged over most of Europe. Now only a small herd is left. It is slightly smaller and markedly less shaggy than the North American bison or buffalo.

The European wild boar is three feet at the shoulder and four feet in length with a tail six inches long. It has a coarse bristly coat of long blackish hair, and the young are striped. This is one of the species from which domestic pigs are derived. It was exterminated in Britain in the sixteenth century, but it is still not uncommon in the forests of France, Germany and other parts of Europe. In many of these places it is treated as game and shot, after being driven from cover by beaters.

The largest of the European deer, the European elk, is slightly smaller than the closely related North American moose. It has smaller antlers than the moose, but otherwise the two species are very much alike in appearance and habit. The elk spends much of its time in summer in the marshes and lakes of northern Europe, especially Finland, wading for water lilies and aquatic vegetation. In winter it migrates to the birch forests to browse the shoots and branches of the saplings.

The red deer of Europe, very closely related to the elk or wapiti of North America, stands four feet or more at the shoulder and has ten- or twelve-tined antlers, up to forty-three inches long when fully grown. Called the "Barbary stag", it is the only deer in Africa. In Britain, where the forests have largely been eliminated, the red deer have largely been compelled to become grazers on moorland although they are by nature browsers on forest foliage. As a consequence, they grow to a smaller size than the red deer in the larger forests of continental Europe. The single spotted calf is born in the late spring and is soon able to accompany the hind as she moves about for pasture. Stags take about twelve years to reach their maximum development, but after twelve years of age the antlers begin to deteriorate so that a very old stag will have poor antlers.

The smallest native deer in Europe is the roe, twenty-six to thirty inches at the shoulder. The bucks have short, three-tined antlers seldom more than twelve inches long. These drop at the end of the year and grow back by February, whereas in most deer their loss and renewal does not take place until spring and summer respectively. A second distinctive feature of the roe deer is its seasonal change of coat. In summer it has a short, bright, fox-red pelage, without a white tail patch. The winter coat is long, thick and dark, speckled greyish-fawn with a very conspicuous tail patch. Living alone or in pairs, in large woods adjoining grassland or fields, the roe deer usually hide by day, coming out at

(opposite page)

(top left)
The European **bison** once roamed in fierce herds in swampy forests. Today, less than 500 of this species, descended from the lowland variety, survive. The smaller and lighter mountain bison is now completely extinct.

(top right)
The tusks of the **wild boar** are actually its canine teeth. This creature snorts loudly, eats anything and everything, and loves to wallow in the mud.

(center, left)
Roe deer are the smallest native deer in Europe. Their ability to hide in undergrowth, coming out at night to feed, allows them to multiply even in heavily cultivated districts.

(center, right)
There is some doubt as to the ancestry of the domestic **sheep.** Domestication probably took place in Asia, but it is possible that the mouflon was crossed with the Asian variety at some time in history.

(bottom left)
Wild goats, or ibex, are still to be found in scattered areas, but interbreeding with domestic goats has greaty reduced the numbers of purebred ibex. The **wild goat of Crete,** with three-ringed horns, is considered to be a pure, or nearly pure, wild species.

(bottom right)
The massive horns of the **mouflon,** or **wild sheep,** are much larger than those of the domesticated species. These small mountain sheep are very quick, sure-footed and agile.

night to feed. Their action when moving is in active bounding, for they are great jumpers. This is seldom seen, however, as they are difficult to drive from cover. During the mating season, in July and August, the bucks and does meet in an open grassy spot and wear a circular track—a "roe ring"—in the course of their mating play, during which time they pair off. Two, sometimes three, spotted fawns are born at a time.

Sheep and Goats

THE ONLY EUROPEAN WILD SHEEP, the mouflon, twenty-seven inches at the shoulder, has a striking pattern of reddish brown with a conspicuous whitish saddle patch and black marks on the limbs. The horns, up to thirty-four inches long, form a close spiral with tips sometimes curving inward. Mouflon live in the most rugged mountainous areas, but continuous persecution by man has reduced their numbers. It seems likely that their best hope for survival lies in their having been introduced to various mountain ranges of Central Europe. Another wild sheep, the red sheep of Cyprus, is a little larger than the mouflon, generally reddish brown, and the females are without horns.

The domestic goat has gone feral in many places in Europe, and there is a strain in Crete which is very close to the original wild stock, and indeed may be said to represent it.

The ibex, a truly wild goat, is found in south-western Europe. It has wide sweeping horns which form an open semi-spiral, and a parti-hued coat. In the past it inhabited most of the mountain ranges of Portugal and Spain, as well as the Pyrenees. The Portuguese and Pyrenean forms are probably now extinct. The Spanish race owed its survival to state protection, after being nearly exterminated about 1905, but it seems probable that the Civil War may have had a bad effect on the ibex stocks. In the Alps of Switzerland, France, Italy and Austria live a limited number of Alpine ibex, small animals less than three feet at

(bottom left)
The **Alpine ibex,** or **wild goat of the Alps,** was hunted nearly out of existence until the middle of the nineteenth century, when only a few were left in the Italian Alps and elsewhere in the mountains. This nearly beardless species has now been reintroduced into several mountainous areas in Southern Europe.

(bottom right)
Small herds of **chamois** live on steep, rocky slopes of mountains in Southern Europe. Members of the family of goat-antelopes, they are extremely agile and can cover over 20 feet in a single leap.

the shoulder and with horns up to thirty-five inches long. It is believed to have been exterminated as a wild animal in most of its haunts, though it has since been reintroduced to many of the Alpine valleys. Because it interbreeds freely with the domestic goat, however, it is very doubtful whether the present stock of Alpine ibex is of pure blood.

The chamois belongs to what are known as the goat-antelopes. It is a small but sturdy animal with the tips of the erect horns abruptly turned over into hooks. It lives in the Alps and a few other mountain ranges in southern Europe as well as in Asia Minor. Preserved as a sporting animal, it is usually found in small parties at the upper edge of the tree line, going higher up the mountains in summer.

► *These primates stayed close to their original home and were forced to develop agility and coordination.*

Monkeys and Apes

Man's closest and cleverest relatives in the animal kingdom are the *primates*—the monkeys and apes. "Primate" means "first", and primates are the first of all animals in intelligence. In other ways —sight, hearing, strength, sense of smell—they are surpassed by many others, but in brain primates stand at the head of the class.

They are not all equal in intelligence. The lemurs are only a little ahead of most other mammals, while the apes show almost manlike abilities in the way they pile one object on another in order to reach food hanging above them. Ounce for ounce, the monkeys have the most brain weight compared to body size. The orangutan has the brain most like man's own.

Man himself is a primate—we might call him the "super-primate". He is not, as some people still think, descended from monkeys and apes, but from an unknown common ancestor. His intelligence has enabled him to spread over the earth and live wherever he pleases, turning all kinds of things into food, clothing and other necessities. But apart from man, the primates have stayed close to their original home, which is in the tropics, all around the equatorial belt of the earth.

Except for a few species like the baboon, most primates dwell in the trees. Agility and co-ordination are very important to any creature living in trees, and the skill the monkeys and apes have developed in

Simultaneous development of hands and brain has made primates "first" among animals. Nimble hands enable them to bring food to their mouths instead of lowering their heads to feed; this frees the eyes and other senses to guard against enemy attack. With the exception of baboons, most primates are tree-dwelling animals. Sacred to the ancient Egyptians, the **hamadryas baboon** (top right) is careful not to let its young stray too far.

moving through the branches has apparently contributed to their mental progress.

Large brains are not the only noteworthy thing about the primates. Most of them have five fingers or toes on each limb, with nails like man's to protect the tips. Most have a thumb set apart from the other fingers, permitting them to grasp branches firmly. Also, they can swing their arms freely either forward or backward. Though most move on all fours, the highest-ranking members of the group often walk erect, like man.

Many other important characteristics vary greatly among the different species. Some are good swimmers. Most have exceptional eyesight, with large eyes set well forward in the face, helping them penetrate the dense jungle in front of them as they move swiftly through it. Some can distinguish various hues, with good depth perception—in other words, they see things very much the way we do.

The apes have no tail, or only the beginning of one, but most of the others have long, well-developed tails, very useful in the trees. Most have distinctive, and usually loud, voices. The gorilla has a guttural roar, the chimpanzee a gruff bark. The gibbon and the howler monkey can be heard a mile off. Most of the smaller monkeys make a whistling noise, often plaintive in tone.

A last distinctive characteristic of nearly all monkeys and apes is that they like to live in groups—either families or whole troops, which live together, hunt and feed in the same area, and battle any outsiders who try to invade their home ground.

A convenient way to divide up the hundreds of kinds of primates is into three large groups: the *prosimians*, the *monkeys* and the *great apes*. The word "prosimian" means "before the monkeys". The six families that make up the prosimians are monkey-like creatures who have been on earth longer than any of their relatives. The monkeys include three families, Old World monkeys, New World monkeys and

(bottom left)
Most **primates** have five fingers and five toes. An opposable thumb set apart from the other fingers and soft pads on the undersides of fingertips and the ends of toes improve their grasp on branches. In comparing the hands and feet of men and monkeys, note especially the greater flexibility of the monkey's foot.

(bottom right)
Hardy and prolific, the **ring-tailed lemur** is the only lemur which can be exported from Madagascar. The government rigidly protects the unique wildlife of the island.

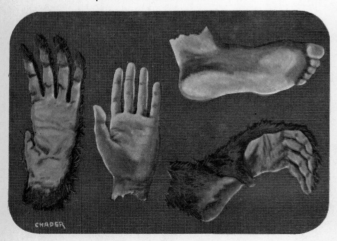

marmosets. The great apes comprise a single family. So, incidentally, does man himself.

The Tree Shrews

THE CURIOUS LITTLE TREE SHREW was the first primate of all, and has many of the characteristics of the Insectivora, the large order of mammals from which the primates evolved. All species of tree shrews live in south-eastern Asia, from India, China and the Malay Peninsula down through the islands of Indonesia. At first glance you might mistake a tree shrew for a squirrel. The commonest species has a bushy tail, large eyes and small but prominent ears. Unlike a squirrel, though, it has a long, slender snout, which it pokes into every nook and cranny in its busy search for insects and fruit. It sits up on its haunches to eat, and after a meal licks its paws and washes its face. It likes water —not only to drink but to bathe in. Both males and females are fighters, with the female especially aggressive before the birth of young. In captivity she may injure or even kill her mate unless he is removed to another cage. In the forest he gets out of her way at an early date. Either will fight to the death any strange shrew that invades their domain.

Lemurs

THE BIGGEST GROUP of prosimians are the lemurs. Yet nearly all of them live on the single large island of Madagascar, off the east coast of Africa. A few are found on smaller islands in the Indian Ocean. The most typical lemurs are about the size of a cat, with long, bushy tails and long snouts that give them a doglike look. They mostly sleep all day in trees and feed at night. Active and nimble, they can make great leaps both in trees and on the ground. One species, the variegated lemur, not only lives in trees but makes nests. Another, the dwarf lemur, "estivates"—that is, he sleeps all summer. Still another, the ring-tailed lemur, differs from all the others in that he is active by day instead of by night.

(left)
Most primitive of the primates, **tree shrews** have traits of both shrews and lemurs. Like shrews, they have long, pointed snouts and are fierce fighters. Their tree-dwelling habits, however, and some physical features are more like those of lemurs.

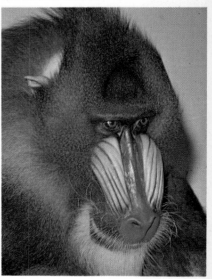

(above)
With canine teeth as large as those of a timber wolf, the **mandrill** is a fearsome adversary. Close relatives of the savannah-dwelling baboons, colorful mandrill troops range the floor of the great Gaboon forest of West Africa. The spectacular face markings are found only on the males.

(top)
Sometimes hanging upside down from branches, the **slow loris** gradually creeps through its rain forest habitat, grasping each limb with deliberate firmness. The large eyes indicate that it is active at night.

(above)
Though mostly arboreal, the **white-handed gibbon** is the only ape that can habitually walk upright on its hind legs. When it uses its hands for locomotion in trees, small quantities of food can be carried by the feet.

(opposite page, bottom, left and right)
One of the few nocturnal lemurs, the **aye-aye** uses its long fingers to tap the bark of trees. When the insects inside begin to move around, the aye-aye reaches in with the long, slender, specialized third finger and probes them out. Long ago, a giant species lived in southwest Madagascar, but it is now extinct. The peculiar, rodentlike teeth of this strange-looking animal once led to its misclassification.

Indris

ANOTHER PRIMATE FAMILY which makes its home on the island of Madagascar includes the avahi, the sifaka and the indri. In Malagasy, "indri" means "look". When the natives pointed out these human-like little tree dwellers to the first Europeans, they said "Indri!" and the Europeans thought this was the animal's name. Indris eat only vegetation, and have fewer teeth than other primates.

In several ways, the species differ. The true indri has a tail so short it is hardly noticeable. The avahi is a night prowler only three feet long including a tail as long as head and body put together. The sifaka has a well-developed tail, and makes a good bit of noise.

Aye-ayes

A THIRD PROSIMIAN of Madagascar looks like something made up of leftover parts of other animals. About the size of a small cat, the aye-aye (his name comes from his cry) has a face vaguely reminiscent of a rat's, with a single pair of prominent incisor teeth in each jaw. On each paw it has ten fingers or toes, long, thin and bony, something like a bird's claws. The third finger of each hand is even thinner than the others. The aye-aye has a long, bushy tail and membranous ears. Mammary glands of females are located low on the abdomen, instead of on the chest as in nearly all other primates.

There are good reasons for the aye-aye's physical peculiarities. It feeds primarily on the adults and larvae of insects that live in trees. At night the aye-aye drums on the bark of a tree with its long fingers to stir up the insects. The insects begin to move around, and the aye-aye, with its acute sense of hearing, detects them. It reaches in with its slender third finger and fishes out the insect. If it cannot reach into the insect's crevice it gnaws through the wood, using its strong incisors until it reaches its prey. The middle finger is useful in other ways—to comb its hair, clean its face and ears, and to bring water to its mouth —it can average forty strokes a minute in spooning water from a pan.

Lorises, Bushbabies and Pottos

THE DOZEN OR SO SPECIES of the loris family fall into three groups: the bushbabies, the pottos and the true lorises. The bushbabies and pottos are native to Africa, while the lorises are found in Southeast Asia and nearby islands. It is easy to see that the lorises and pottos are related, because they look very much alike. But only a zoologist would guess that the bushbabies are their close cousins. Long-tailed, and propelled by strong legs designed for leaping, the bushbabies do not show much physical resemblance to the rest of the family. Their habits, though, are the same—they live in the forest, mostly in the tree

Lemurs evolved long before true monkeys. At that time, Africa and Madagascar were bridged together, and lemurs roamed throughout. Although they are extinct in Africa, they have survived and diversified in Madagascar. **Peters' dwarf lemur** (top left), actually a mouse lemur, is the only primate that "*estivates*," or sleeps through the summer. Most dwarf lemurs are ground-dwellers and live in holes, but the **fork marked dwarf lemur** (top right) builds squirrel-like nests in trees. The sad, ghostly wailing of the **indri** (left), another inhabitant of Madagascar, resounds through the rain forests, each animal singing on a different key, creating a strange harmony.

(top left)
Rolled up in a hollow during the day, the **slender loris** is active only at night, when it moves slowly through the trees, searching for insects.

(top right)
Moving in slow motion, the **potto** carefully approaches its prey and, when close enough to attack, makes a quick grab with its hands. It is fond of grasshoppers and lizards.

(opposite page, bottom)
Among the primates, which range from the squirrel-sized tree shrew to the 550-pound gorilla, the variety of shapes and physical characteristics is astounding. Tree shrews have sharp claws. Lemurs have foxlike snouts. Gorillas support themselves on their knuckles. Gibbons have long, slender arms. The spider monkey has a tail with which it can grasp things. Tarsiers have adhesive pads on their fingers and toes.

branches, sleep during the day and at night feed on small animals and insects, fruits and vegetables.

The slow loris of South-east Asia and nearby islands is a heavyset creature which is never in any hurry. Its fur is short and woolly and usually rusty-grey. It has a dark ring around each of its large eyes (in some the rings extend up the forehead, where they may join), and a whitish line between which extends downward toward the nose. The big toes and thumbs are set at right angles to the other toes and fingers, providing good ability to grasp, which is important to a slow-moving dweller in the treetops. Often it inches its way along a branch hanging upside down. When it sees an insect or lizard, it makes a sudden lunge, while holding tight to the branch with its hind feet.

Smaller than the slow loris is the slender loris of Ceylon and southern India. It is a trimmer, longer-limbed version of its cousin but, like it, no speedster.

Two species of pottos live in Africa. Like the lorises, one is larger and chunkier, the other smaller, longer-legged and more graceful. The first, the common potto, has large, broad hands and feet which can grasp a branch solidly. This potto moves slowly most of the time, even when it is stalking an insect or lizard, but when it gets close enough the potto makes a swift grab and usually gets its meal. The potto's tail is about a fifth the length of its head and body but seems to serve no particular purpose. Its most remarkable physical feature is a sharp row of bony spikes running down its spine. The potto can either keep these spikes hidden in its fur or bare them for action. When an enemy threatens, the potto suddenly doubles over with its head between its legs, dealing a ripping downward blow at the adversary. The potto is equipped with very strong hands, giving it the most powerful grip of any creature of its size.

The golden potto, smaller and slighter in build, has a longer, more pointed snout, and a mere nubbin of a tail hidden in its fur. A line

(right)
The **galago** urinates on its hands and feet to give itself an adhesive grip on branches. This night creature also marks the branches of its territory with urine.

(left)
Long hind legs act much like springs for the tiny **pigmy bushbaby.** Almost bouncing, the bushbaby makes tremendous leaps to catch food or escape enemies.

TREE SHREW

LEMUR

SLOW LORIS

TARSIER

SPIDER
MONKEY

GIBBON

GORILLA

down the middle of its snout gives a hint of its relationship to the bushbaby and the slow loris.

The various species of bushbaby (also known as galagos) come in a number of sizes, from the two-and-a-half-foot great galago down to the tiny pygmy bushbaby, which is only ten inches long including a five-inch tail. All bushbabies are large-eared, big-eyed acrobats with large feet suited for leaping. And leap they do, sometimes over great distances from one branch to another. The long tail helps them keep their balance. A jumping bushbaby whips it about in midair to stay on course. Bushbabies frequently call to each other in a loud, ringing cry (which is probably why they are called babies). Their highly sensitive ears are most useful in locating insects and small animals. They constantly turn this way and that to locate new sounds.

Tarsiers

THE LITTLE TARSIERS, most of which are only six inches long, look so much like tiny goblins that one of the species has been given the Latin name *spectrum*, meaning ghost. Tarsiers look much like bushbabies, but lack the kittenish appeal of their cousins. Their owl-like eyes are even larger, but seem always to stare; their fingers and toes are longer, and knobby, and their tails are naked. One naturalist said that the bushbabies look like little angels and the tarsiers like little devils.

The tarsiers are strictly carnivorous, feeding entirely on small animals and insects. They apparently do not make nests, and most of them found in the daytime are sound asleep grasping tightly to a branch. The three species, all very much alike in appearance, live in forests on islands from the Philippines to Sumatra.

(above)
Olive baboons have a pronounced social order within their troops, with the older, stronger males acting as leaders and protectors. Even powerful opponents, such as leopards, have been killed by groups of males defending their troop against attack. This baboon is performing lookout duty in a tree.

(right)
Coming down occasionally to eat fallen fruits, the **red uacari** prefers to stay in the treetops. Rather grotesque-looking, this monkey has scanty hair growth that leaves much of its pallid, pink skin exposed, especially around the head.

Titi monkeys have a monkeylike posture, but their movements and voices are more like those of the marmosets. Unlike other monkeys, they have claws instead of nails and sleep in holes in trees.

(below)
Serving as a fifth hand, the prehensile tail of the **spider monkey** can clasp branches and even reach for fruits and other food. This ability is characteristic of only one group of New World monkeys.

New World Monkeys

THE PROSIMIANS we have discussed so far have been "monkey-like" rather than real monkeys. The true monkeys—the Old World monkeys, the New World monkeys and the marmosets—are more familiar to most people.

Among the best known of the acrobatic New World monkeys are the sapajous, or capuchin monkeys, once commonly seen on the street-corners of American cities as organ-grinders' pets. Squirrel monkeys are sold in pet shops today, but most New World monkeys are seen only in zoos, for they are delicate and require great care in captivity.

All the New World monkeys live in the trees, but apart from this they vary too much for easy generalization. Most of them are active by day, and most have long tails, but there are exceptions even to these descriptions. The sapajous fall into two main groupings—the horned sapajous and plain-headed sapajous. The horned sapajous do not have horns, but thick tufts of hair on their heads. The plain-heads are usually recognizable by the very light face, chest and shoulders in contrast to the dark body. All the sapajous can curl their tails up, which has given them the nickname of "ringtails". But although the tails are "prehensile"—strong enough to grasp things by—they are not strong enough to hang by, as some people believe.

Very different is the douroucouli, the only true monkey which shuns the light of day. Its eyes are enormous, with a white patch over each. Another New World monkey, the titi, is very similar to the douroucouli, except that it does its sleeping at night and its hunting in the daytime, and so has eyes of normal size. Both titis and douroucoulis eat meat, fruit and vegetables, and especially relish insects. As the douroucouli roams through the trees it utters a loud, catlike cry, which has led to its nickname of "devil monkey". Actually, the douroucouli can be very useful to man. Made a pet in many South American homes, it keeps the house clear of giant spiders, centipedes, cockroaches and mice.

Uacaris and sakis, both of which live in the Great Amazon Basin of South America, are really close cousins, although they look very different from each other. Uacaris are the only New World monkeys with short tails—at first glance it looks as if a uacari's tail has been cut off halfway down. One species of uacari has long auburn hair, another a whitish coat with a rusty tinge. In both the top of the head is covered with very short hair, so short the monkeys look bald. Even more noticeable are their flaming red faces. In captivity their faces fade somewhat unless they are exposed to a good bit of sunlight. Because the uacari is popular as a pet, natives often capture them, using an ingenious method. They shoot the monkey with a poisoned arrow, catch it as it falls, and feed it a pinch of salt, the antidote for the poison.

Like the uacaris, sakis have a coat of long hair which conceals a spindly build, but the sakis have long tails. Some species have bangs on their foreheads, and beards, giving them a sort of "Beatle" or "beatnik" look. In another species the males have a circular white disc around the face.

Spider monkeys owe their name to the peculiar way they walk on their long, spidery legs and arms. Their toes are long enough to serve as extra sets of fingers, and their two-foot-long tails have so good a grip that they can hang by them, while using all four hands to search for food. Sometimes the spider monkey reverses the process and picks up an object with its tail, in much the same way as an elephant does with its trunk. The tail has a longer reach than the arms or legs. Once at the Bronx Zoo a keeper occupied in a repair job left his tools near a spider monkey's cage, taking care to put them out of reach of the

(bottom left)
Along the southeast coast of Brazil is a belt of forest, isolated from the mainland jungles, containing many species of **marmosets.** Some species were once the favored pets of courtesans, who kept them nestled in their bosoms.

(bottom right)
Also called "night ape" or "owl monkey" the large-eyed **douroucouli** is the only nocturnal primate of the New World. It is a shy, gentle animal.

WOOLLY MONKEY

SQUIRREL MONKEY

CAPUCHIN MONKEY

MARMOSET

(top left)
Though prolific and long-lived, the mortality rate of the **squirrel monkey** is high. Those that live to reach full maturity can be four times the size of the average adult. Pet dealers, however, have overflooded the market, and unless restrictions are put on capture and export of these monkeys from South America, it may soon be too late to save them.

(top right)
Thriving in captivity, the **capuchin monkey** is well known as the organ-grinder's companion and is the most common monkey found in zoos. The favorite of pet shops, it learns quickly to imitate the antics of man.

Throughout the jungles of South America live a profusion of primates quite different from their distant relatives of the Old World. The New World monkeys have three premolars and round nostrils set far apart, and some have prehensile tails. The marmosets have such primitive features as claws on all the fingers and nonopposable thumbs.

(right)
Best known for its uproarious, ear-rending call, the **red howler** is among the largest of South American monkeys. The howls are usually made by one individual and are produced through a spherically-shaped sound box in the back of the throat.

(below)
Isolated on Madagascar and the Comoro Islands, lemurs vary greatly in size, shape and behavior. The **black lemur,** though completely arboreal (tree-dwelling), frequently comes to the ground when molested.

monkey's hands and feet. But the monkey thrust its tail between the bars and snatched one of the tools.

Larger than the spider monkeys are the woolly monkeys. They are not shaggy like most of their cousins, but are clad in a dark brown or black coat of short, dense, woolly hair. Less spindly than the spider monkeys, with thick bodies, they are sometimes called *barrigudos* (pot-bellies) by the South American natives. Like the spiders, they have useful tails. Of all the New World monkeys, they are the most docile in captivity, but require exceptionally good care.

A rare combination is the woolly spider monkey of south-eastern Brazil, a light tan monkey with woolly coat and long limbs. Little is known about this species, though it is a fairly safe guess that like its cousins it lives in small groups of a dozen or so individuals, and spends most of its time in the trees.

The last of the monkeys with prehensile tails are the howler monkeys, who are also the largest of the group. Their tails are exceptionally strong, and despite their size they can hang by them. The various species of howlers are black, rusty and brownish. Their hair is thick and dense, and their jutting jaws make them look rather fierce. Equipped with a larynx, or voice box, much bigger than those of any of their relatives, they fill the forest with loud, ringing calls. Usually only a half dozen or fewer howlers live together, but sometimes a troop of thirty or forty band together, which makes a fairly noisy forest community.

Squirrel monkeys are the light-faced, dark-crowned little animals with almost black noses and mouths which are commonly sold in pet shops. The two species, one from northern South America, the other from Central America, look very much alike. They often band to-gether in large troops, sometimes of a hundred or more.

If this book had been written a few years ago our list of New World monkeys would be regarded as complete at this point. But there is a small black animal called the callimico, which in some ways resembles

the New World monkeys and in some ways the marmosets which we will describe next. Recently scientists have been able to observe a pair of callimicos in captivity, and the way in which they cared for their baby was that of the New World monkeys. The mother carried the baby around with her, unlike the marmosets, which have a very characteristic baby-raising system of their own.

Marmosets

In the forests of South and Central America dwell a huge family of small primates that barely qualify as monkeys. Marmosets are small, even for monkeys, the smallest being no bigger than good-sized mice, and the largest not much bigger than squirrels. The pygmy marmoset has a body six inches long, and a slightly longer tail. The pygmy is generally a greyish brown, in contrast to the bigger marmosets, whose hair tufts come in striking patterns of black, reddish, yellow-tinged, grey-brown and white.

Another group of marmosets, the tamarins, are alike in that they have long canine teeth in the lower jaw, but otherwise differ in many ways. Many species have almost bare faces. The cotton-top marmoset has a bushy mane of white hair, while Geoffroy's marmoset has a narrow ridge of white hair on top of its head. The most impressive member of this group is the emperor marmoset, which sports an enormous white handlebar moustache.

The golden marmoset and its two black relatives are the largest members of the family. The coat of the golden is a bright metallic orange-gold, and a heavy mane hides the ears, giving the little monkey the look of a tiny lion.

In habits the marmosets are all very much alike. While they feed mainly on insects, they also eat quantities of fruit. But the most remarkable of marmoset habits has to do with the method of raising

(top left)
Crowns of stiff white hairs circle each ear of the **ruffed marmoset,** the first marmoset discovered in the New World. Its name was passed on to this whole group of primates.

(top right)
Orange-red fur adorns this silky **marmoset.** All marmosets are small-bodied, the smallest being the size of a mouse and the largest not much bigger than a squirrel.

(below)
A denizen of the equatorial forests of South America, the **spider monkey** has very long limbs that enable it to swing swiftly through the treetops. When hanging by its tail, it has a spiderlike appearance.

the offspring. When a baby marmoset is born the father rather than the mother carries it around, only handing it to the mother for nursing.

Old World Monkeys

MORE NUMEROUS than the New World monkeys and marmosets put together are the dozens of species of Old World monkeys, most of whom dwell in Africa and Asia, with one species occupying a small area of Europe. All the Old World monkeys are much alike, even though they differ widely in appearance. They fall into four main groups: baboons, macaques, guenons and leaf monkeys. All, in true monkey fashion, live together in bands.

Baboons are large, ground-dwelling monkeys of Africa, whose faces are lengthened into snouts. The males are much bigger than the females, and usually different in appearance. Dog-faced baboons, which roam the open country and woodland south of the Sahara, are brownish, with variations, and have dusky brown faces. The forest-dwelling mandrill of West Africa is by contrast a gaudy creature, or at least the adult male is. Its body fur is a rich olive brown, and it wears a yellow-orange beard. The muzzle is brilliant blue, with a scarlet central line and nose. Showing through the sparse hair of the buttocks is an area of skin that blends tones of red and violet. Females and young have blackish faces.

The hamadryas, sacred baboon of the ancient Egyptians, sports a pale coat that blends with the light soil tone of north-east Africa and Arabia. As in other baboons, the male is far larger than the female, and wears a heavy mane.

The gelada baboon of Ethiopia is perhaps the oddest of its clan. Its nostrils open more toward the sides of its nose than do those of other baboons, and its chest is marked by a large patch of bare skin shaped like a dumbbell.

Baboons are among the most intelligent as well as the most sociable of monkeys. Herds of several hundred are not unusual. They have no fixed dwelling place, but restrict themselves to a definite area in their

(above)
A bright orange-gold mane flows back from the small, blue-eyed face of the **golden marmoset**, giving it the look of a tiny lion.

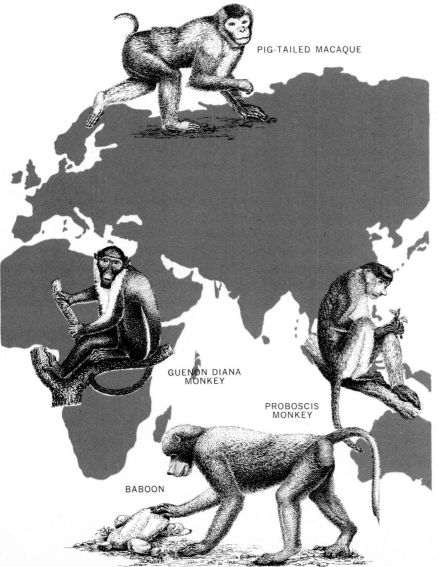

PIG-TAILED MACAQUE

GUENON DIANA
MONKEY

PROBOSCIS
MONKEY

BABOON

(top left)
Inhabiting the savannahs and open woodlands of tropical Africa, baboons are large, ground-dwelling monkeys with strongly social behavior. The **yellow baboon** makes its home in the woodlands of Central Africa.

(top right)
Very combative, the **gelada baboon** sometimes comes in contact with bands of other kinds of baboons. Huge battles ensue, which include such tactics as sneak attack and prisoner-taking.

Although they may once have had a common ancestor, the Old World monkeys have evolved separately from those of the New World for a very long time. They have two premolars and comma-shaped nostrils that point downwards, and some have naked, brightly colored rumps. These primates include baboons, macaques, guenons and leaf monkeys.

The arid Guaso Nyiro River valley in Kenya harbors a virtual panorama of African wildlife. Waterholes in the area become meccas for many animals that otherwise are usually not found in association with each other. The reticulated giraffe is a subspecies found throughout the plains regions of Africa. There are approximately sixty forms of true gazelles in the world, and the Grant's gazelle is one of the largest and carries the longest horns. The Grevy zebra is the largest of the zebras and also has the largest ears. Other animals in the area pictured here are a troop of baboons, warthogs, elephants, impalas, elands, rhinos, gerenuks and black-backed jackals.

roaming. They are polygamous, and one male may have as many as seven wives. Very combative, they will sometimes fight to the death over a female, even killing the female herself. When the herd is on the move the oldest males take the lead, with the younger males forming a rear guard. Sometimes bachelors form their own herd.

Macaques are probably the most familiar monkeys to most people. One, the rhesus monkey, is not only commonly seen in pet shops and circuses, but is the monkey most often used in medical research. Over a dozen other species of macaques exist, mostly in southern Asia. They are generally robust, medium-sized to large brown monkeys with tails that vary among the species from very long to very short. The pig-tailed macaque has a short, curly tail. Only two species of macaques are found far from the Asian mainland. One lives on the southernmost Japanese islands, the other, curiously enough, on the rock of Gibraltar. This is the Barbary ape, which also inhabits the North African coast. Legend has it that when the Barbary apes leave Gibraltar, British dominion there will end, so the British garrison takes pains to see that the monkeys are well cared for.

Four species of macaques who dwell in central Africa are known as mangabeys, owing to an error by early naturalists who associated them

with a place in Madagascar. Actually the mangabeys have never lived on that island. They are monkeys of slender build, with whitish eyelids that contrast with their dark faces. One, the cherry-top mangabey, has a reddish crown.

The third group of Old World monkeys are the guenons. Though the dozen species are all closely related, they vary widely in markings and appearance. They have faces adorned with ruffs, beards, stripes, patches of bright blue skin. All have long, graceful tails, some black, some white, some red and as you may guess from that fact, all are agile forest dwellers. Yet two species, Allen's swamp monkey and the patas monkey, have both developed a preference for the ground, the former living in swamps and the latter in open areas. The patas has long legs, and runs as nimbly as a dog.

The guenons are popular attractions at the zoo, and delight crowds for hours with their acrobatics and mischief. At one zoo a guenon was given a medicine containing alcohol at certain hours fixed by a veterinarian. When it recovered, it had developed a fondness for the medicine, and whenever the former hour for treatment arrived, it put its hands to its belly and moaned and begged.

The last group of Old World monkeys can be lumped under the

(top left)
Once threatened with extinction, the **black and white colobus** were killed in enormous numbers for their fur. This race occupies low elevation forests of East Africa and the Congo.

(top right)
At sunset, the **black and white colobus** sit in large groups in the tops of high forest trees. A leaf-eater, the colobus has a cowlike compartment stomach that aids in the digestion of plant matter.

(above, left)
Thriving in India and the Himalayas, the **entellus monkey** is the sacred monkey of the Hindus. At high elevations, it can sometimes be seen frolicking in the snow.

(above, right)
Perhaps the strangest-looking monkey of all is the **proboscis monkey** of Borneo. The male has an enormous, pendulous nose, as much as three inches long, which hangs down over the mouth. The use of this nose is unknown, although it gives the voice a nasal quality.

Many guenons, like the **moustached monkey,** have clownlike faces and delight zoo-goers with their acrobatics and mischief.

term leaf monkeys. Most live in Asia and the islands, but there are some in Africa, too. Among them are the colobus, the langur, and the strange-looking proboscis monkey. The colobus and the langur have stomachs compartmented like a cow's, and live almost entirely on leaves. One kind of colobus, the bishop monkey, has a long coat of silky fur, in dark and light shades. At one time its coat threatened to cause the animal's extinction, so popular was it for trimming women's hats and coats. Nearly two million monkeys were destroyed before the fad for "monkey fur" died out.

Some species of langur are quite hardy, and have been seen on the snow-covered slopes of the Himalayas. Rarest of this group are the snub-nosed langurs of the high mountains of China. Little is known of their habits, but they resemble the true langurs in most respects, except for their turned-up noses.

The last of the leaf monkey group is by all odds the strangest, both in looks and in habits. The proboscis monkey of Borneo is reddish-brown above and buff below, with a tail as long as its head and body together. But much the most striking feature of the male's appearance is an enormous, pendulous nose, utterly unlike that of any other monkey. Sometimes it is as much as three inches long, and hangs below the monkey's chin. A dweller in swampy country, the proboscis monkey is unusual in another respect. It likes to swim and does it very well.

The Great Apes

NEXT TO MAN, the most intelligent of all animals are the great apes, a family of medium-sized to large primates which includes the chimpanzees, the gorillas, the orangutans and the gibbons. All are tail-less, and all are characterized by long, powerful arms that can easily support the weight of the body. The legs are shorter, and too weak to launch the animal in a long jump, but it can swing from tree to tree with ease. When they walk on all fours they do not put their hands on the ground in the manner of monkeys, but support their weight on bent knuckles of fingers and on the outer edges of the soles of the feet. Their thumbs are freely jointed at the wrist, as in the human hand.

Comfort lovers, they often build nests as temporary or overnight sleeping places. Each animal makes its own, and the female takes a nursing baby into her nest with her.

In recent years field studies by zoologists who virtually lived with their subjects have uncovered fascinating new evidence of ape intelligence. Chimpanzees have been seen probing into termite nests with blades of grass. When the termites attacked and held on to the stems, the chimps withdrew the grass and ate the insects. This use of objects as tools has been seen under artificial conditions in laboratories, but never before in the wild, for apes are by nature shy and difficult to approach.

The chimpanzee is without question the best known of the manlike apes, both to scientists and to the public. Young chimps perform in circuses and on television, often with their facial hair shaved, and often wearing human clothing, giving them the appearance of grotesque men. But it is in zoos that one can better appreciate their natural personalities. A mature male chimpanzee weighs as much as a man, usually about 170 pounds, and occasionally as much as 200 pounds. Females are smaller. In their equatorial African home chimps are found over a wide area, and so are more frequently captured than the other apes. In addition, they are generally hardier in captivity and easier to care for. But even if it were not for these things, chimpanzees would probably be the most popular, because they are most like men. Unlike the pensive gorilla and the phlegmatic orangutan, the chimp seems to enjoy the reaction of an audience, and is always ready to show off his intelligence. Probably the most intelligent, and certainly the most teachable of the apes, he can learn to ride a bicycle, hammer a nail, dress and undress, eat with a fork and many other things.

The usual method of capturing a chimpanzee in the wild is to fell all the trees around him, isolating him in a single tree. Then he is forced into a net, though he may resist savagely, and is quite capable of killing a man with his long canine teeth.

Besides two full-sized chimpanzees, the bald-headed and long-haired, there is the rarely seen pygmy chimpanzee, a miniature version of the species, which lives south of the Congo.

Second of the great apes is the gorilla, a single species, but with two subspecies which live in territories several hundred miles apart. The mountain gorilla of the Congo is larger and longer-haired than its lowland counterpart, whose home is along the west coast of Equatorial Africa, but the habits of the two are very similar.

Gorillas are tremendous in size, especially the males, which may weigh as much as 550 pounds, more than a quarter of a ton. The females are only about half as big. The size is especially surprising in view of the fact that a baby gorilla weighs only about four and a half pounds, scarcely more than half the weight of the average newborn

(bottom left)
Some of the skeletal structures of the gorilla can be compared to man's proportions, however, often differ. (1) The arms of the gorilla are longer than the legs. In man, the legs are longer. (2) Joints at the elbows and wrists allow great flexibility. (3) The crest of the skull and the jaws are more massive than man's. (4) The pelvic bone structure, which aids in an upright posture, is shorter but very similar to man's.

(bottom right)
"Orangutan" means 'man of the forest.' This giant of Southeast Asia has some manlike traits. (1) The jaw bone protrudes. (2). The feet terminate in a heel on which the leg rests. (3) The hands are long and have opposable thumbs.

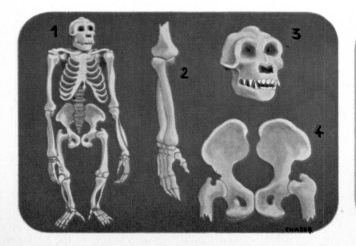

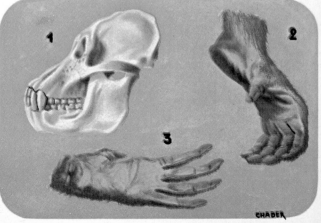

human baby. The gorillas roam in small, loosely organized family bands whose members may from time to time wander off to join other bands. Their day is spent in a leisurely pattern of eating, resting and exploring new territory. As night approaches the females and young retire to the branches of trees and build sleeping nests, while the heavy adult males construct nests on the ground, where they stand guard. If a stranger should intrude, the father gorilla will rise to his feet with a fierce snarl, glare, beat his breast and finally let out a mighty roar. Few animals stay in the vicinity long after hearing this bloodcurdling noise.

One of the oddest facts about the gorilla, considering how well-known an animal it is today, is that a hundred years ago very few people had ever seen one, and even they had confused it with the chimpanzee.

The orangutan and several species of gibbon inhabit South-east Asia and its associated islands. The orangutan is limited to the islands of Borneo and Sumatra, where the expansion of agriculture and other human activity is threatening it with extinction.

The genial and intelligent orangutan is in many ways the oddest of the great apes. Large (200 pounds or more) and clothed in long, shaggy, reddish hair, the males develop broad fleshy facial disks, and an arm-spread of up to seven and a half feet—greater even than the gorilla's—though the body does not exceed four and a half feet. At an even and deliberate pace they swing through the thick forest on those powerful arms, moving faster than a man on the ground can run.

At night the orang builds a sleeping platform of boughs and leaves which it does not leave in the morning until the sun has dried the dew. During the rainy season the comfort-loving animal covers itself with a blanket of leaves.

In captivity the orangutan is happy and can be taught many tricks. Some can not only unlock a door, but pick the right key out of a bunch. Even in captivity they have a long lifetime for apes—up to twenty-five years.

Most agile of the great apes are the gibbons, which swing through the treetops with incredible grace and speed. Their arms are so long that when they stand erect their fingers touch the ground. On the

(bottom left)
Chimpanzees are much more high-strung and excitable than are their close relatives, the gorillas. Their daily routine always includes a session of uproarious hootings and howlings. A small race known as the **pygmy chimpanzee** is found only in the southern Congo.

(bottom right)
Recent behavioral observations in the field have disclosed the extraordinary fact that **chimpanzees** fashion stalks of grass to probe into termite mounds. This actually amounts to tool-making, an ability that only man was thought to possess.

ground this lithe animal appears awkward, holding its long arms over its head and hurrying to keep its balance. In the trees it outswings all other primates. Forewarned, it is safe even from its arch-enemy, the leopard, which occasionally surprises it on the ground.

Gibbons are divided into two groups, the larger consisting of a half dozen species in South-east Asia, varying from light sandy to black in tone. The other is a single species, large in size, native to Sumatra and Malaya. All gibbons, which average fourteen pounds in weight, have tremendous voices for their size. The loud voices permit the animals constantly to proclaim their ownership of a given stretch of forest, through which roves a small group consisting of a single male, several females and the young.

Social Life of the Primates

A NEED FOR THE COMPANY of their fellows is basic to all the primates, except, perhaps, some of the prosimians. All of the apes and monkeys, so far as is known, and many of the lemurs, live in groups of varying size. Isolated pairs are sometimes seen, but groups of ten or more are far more usual, and there have been reports of some species

(top left)
When threatened, the male **gorilla** will often make a false attack, running rapidly toward the enemy while beating his chest and yelling angrily.

(top right)
Too heavy for acrobatics, the **orangutan** moves through the trees with manlike care, often bending branches downward to reach the next tree.

(above left)
At dawn, the **hoolock,** a dark gibbon of Indonesia, begins a whoop-like calling that continues for several hours. The purpose of the call is to proclaim ownership of a certain territory.

(above right)
The graceful **gibbon** can leap a distance of 10 yards, and it is said to be able to change direction in mid-air.

forming groups containing several hundred. The advantages of banding together are considerable. Even the largest male baboon, with its sharp teeth, would stand little chance alone against the larger predators; but a few males fighting as a group can put the most determined leopard to flight, saving themselves and guaranteeing the safety of the females and babies.

Where food is very scarce, as in desert regions, a solitary animal is better equipped to survive than is one which has to share a scanty food supply with a large group that includes young not its own; many desert-dwelling creatures, for this reason, are fiercely antisocial and defend their home territories from intruders. But monkeys live in habitats where vegetation is usually abundant. In addition, most kinds of monkeys will eat almost anything else edible, as well—insects, small vertebrates, roots—so the presence of their fellows causes no food supply problems. And if the troop does strip an area of a particularly desired delicacy, the whole tribe simply moves on to a new area.

Each troop generally stakes out a section of land or forest for its own, and in the tropics this is generally more than adequate for the feeding of its tenants. The method of indicating the boundaries of a territory depends upon the species. The monkeys' lesser cousins, the bushbabies, literally mark their home range with urine, deposited first on the hands and feet and then rubbed on twigs and branches. So strong is this need to mark its territory that a captive bushbaby feels insecure, after its cage has been cleaned, until it has clearly declared its ownership of the branches by its ancestral method. Howler monkeys and gibbons keep interlopers away by filling the air with resounding calls that probably also help scattered members of the troop to remain in contact.

Monkeys which live in lush forests where food is most plentiful are found in larger bands than similar inhabitants of near-desert places where feeding is more of a task. Hamadryas baboons, for example, live in groups of only a few dozen by day; even though several bands may peaceably occupy the same protected sleeping place at night.

A troop of monkeys is often led by a single dominant adult male. Within his troop, such a leader is an absolute monarch, demanding, and getting, the best of everything—the best food, the best sleeping place, and his choice of mates from among the females. While this arrangement might seem unfair, in such species as the baboons the leaders repay their subjects by defending them in battle against their enemies. In all species, however, the leader provides something else very necessary to the peace of mind of the others; by the very fact of being the leader he helps to hold the troop together as a unit, often breaking up fights between subordinate members, and in a sense making decisions for the others, such as choosing the sleeping place for the night or the direction in which the troop will wander during the day. If monkey society were a democratic one, with each individual free to go where it

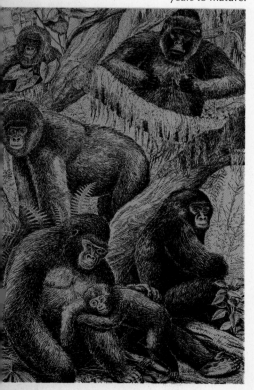

Mistakenly portrayed as a brutal beast, the **gorilla** has a gentle temperament if left in peace. Male gorillas stay with the females and young, and several families band together in groups. They spend their days foraging for fruits and leaves and, at night, build nests of branches and twigs tied with actual knots. Young gorillas take five years to mature.

wished, the troop would soon be widely scattered, and its separated members far more vulnerable to danger. So the tyranny of monkey leadership plays a very important and necessary part in a monkey's life. Each monkey has a definite rank within his troop. He may rise or fall in rank through fighting; but it seems that it is vital to his well-being to be a part of such a system.

Fighting between the members of a troop is regulated by strict "rules". Sometimes a really serious fight breaks out, and the scars on some old males attest to this; but usually fights do no physical damage. Nature has seen to it that animals rarely do real harm to members of their own species, for such battles would result in unnecessary deaths. Most such fights are won and lost without either antagonist receiving even a scratch. How is this done? By bluff and intimidation. Even the monkeys and apes, whose ability to learn by experience has largely replaced instinct in many ways, depend upon instinct at times; and the ritual of fighting with the strict rules of the game, so to speak, is one of those inborn patterns that every animal has.

When it reaches a certain age, even a monkey born in a zoo and raised by humans away from its kind will threaten intruders in the way proper to its species. One form of threat is a direct, fixed stare. Since monkeys and apes never really stare at one another unless a fight is brewing, a stare is a challenge. Frequently a fight is avoided when one of the antagonists looks away, but if this stratagem fails, the monkey may pull back its lips to show its teeth, and follow this with a stiff, jerking movement. Stare hard at an adult male monkey in a zoo sometime and you may be rewarded by a display of threat activity—but don't stand within his reach!

There is a true story about a zoo keeper who had to walk out on an island occupied by baboons every day to clean the exhibit. He was never bothered by the monkeys, but one day he fell ill, and another keeper, unfamiliar with monkeys, took his place. The new man was badly bitten by a large male. What had happened was that the new keeper did not trust the baboons, and kept looking at them, expecting trouble. By looking at them he had invited an attack, for the old keeper knew enough to pretend to ignore the animals, never looking directly at any of them.

In the Bronx Zoo it was necessary one day to introduce two adult gorillas, a male and a female, to one another. Both animals instinctively knew enough not to stare, and in fact would pass each other with their faces turned elaborately away from each other. Eventually the male tried to assert his dominance by a bluff, but the cantankerous old female was not impressed, and began to hammer at him with her fists. By chance, the male's mouth was open, and with one of her blows the female struck his mouth and accidentally gashed her forearm on one of the male's teeth. Then another of the species' instinctive safeguards against serious injury came into play, or at least we believe that it was

Unlike their tree-dwelling cousins, **baboons** have taken to living on the ground, which makes life much more dangerous. To overcome this situation, they live in large troops with a strong social order and rank. Though one great male always reigns supreme, the large, subordinate males are a constant challenge to his position, and a leader must continually assert himself to insure his status. When a troop is threatened by a common enemy, however, all internal strife ceases, and the males cooperate in defending the females and young.

instinctive. The sight of the wound seemed to upset the male, and although he was angered by the attack, he shrank away from the female. For several days, in fact, until the wound healed, the male actively avoided her, and retreated if she approached him.

If primates have evolved a means to keep real combat to a minimum, they have also developed a means to cement friendly relations. Anyone who has watched monkeys in the wild or in a zoo has seen them picking through one another's fur. This "flea-picking" does help monkeys to get rid of fleas, lice and other external parasites, but it also plays a large role in the social life of the group, and is practiced even when no parasites are present. It is a form of grooming, but even more, the groomed monkey is indicating to the one doing the grooming that it trusts the other, and while in other instances the social rank within a troop governs which monkey may approach which, for purposes of grooming they do not take rank into account. Any member of the group may groom any other, as a rule.

Reproduction

MOST PRIMATES have one baby at a time and devote a longer time to raising it than do other mammals. Monkeys and apes sometimes produce twins, but such an occurrence is decidedly rare, except in tree shrews and marmosets, where two or three babies are not unusual. Newborn primates are almost as helpless as human infants, but in many species the baby is born strong enough to grasp firmly to its mother's fur as she carries it about. The young of some of the more primitive kinds are born in a nest, where their mothers leave them while foraging for food. Mother gibbons tuck their knees up as they swing through the treetops, to form a kind of cradle under the baby. When the youngster has grown a bit it often rides pickaback.

Most primate fathers are content only to protect their babies and mates from danger, and to allow the baby to climb on them for a while, but father marmosets are exceptions to the rule. A male marmoset takes over many of the duties of tending his youngsters; he even carries them around for his mate, returning them to her when it is time to nurse them. Even after young marmosets are well grown, their father will quite likely continue to care for them. A male mandrill, on the other hand, will put up with his offspring's antics only while it is very small. At first it can jump on his back or tug at his beard without a reprimand; but the day soon comes when the baby finds its father less tolerant, and it turns to other youngsters in the troop for play.

Only in a few cases, particularly the leaf monkeys, do newborn differ altogether in hue from their parents. Colobus babies are pure white at birth, and langurs may be a bright rusty red. Within a few months, though, the original hair is replaced by new growth which matches that of the adult.

Like humans, most primates have only one baby at a time. Relying less on instincts and more on learned behavior than other mammals, primate mothers must teach their young to guard against predators and to fend for themselves.

The young of most of the lower primates grow rapidly. Tree shrews are ready to set out on their own when they are about a month old, but monkeys and apes mature slowly. This is not surprising if we remember that their lives are governed less than other mammals' by instinct. They require a long period of childhood, during which to learn how to use their brains. Man has the longest childhood, or learning period, of all mammals; but the great apes run a close second; a gorilla, for example, does not become adult until it is five or six years old. During its childhood the young primate gradually learns how to depend on itself—what foods to eat, how to behave with others of its kind, how to recognize and save itself from its enemies, and to some extent how to use the instinctive sounds and gestures it has inherited to communicate with others of its species. While it is learning how to act, the adults of a troop will usually forgive breaches of conduct; but once the primate has grown up, its companions and relatives accept it into their society only if it follows the rules of adult conduct.

Primates and Man

Man's association with other primates is an ancient one. From old tomb paintings, sculpture and mummies, there is evidence that the hamadryas baboon was kept in captivity by the Egyptians, and that it figured in their religion. Even today one of the Hindu gods, Hanuman, is pictured as the monkey god, and the Indian langur is held sacred. A number of the prosimians are regarded with a fear born of superstition by native peoples in the regions where they are found— perhaps because these creatures are active only by night. We can see something akin to this, in other countries, in the unreasonable fear that many people have of bats.

From religious and superstitious origins man's contact with monkeys expanded. Travellers in early days brought monkeys, as well as other

With the look of a wise, old philosopher, the **Brazza monkey** is very neat and tidy: Its snow-white beard is kept combed and cleaned. Grooming is an important activity of monkeys and is used as a sign of affection between individuals.

The male **mandrill** puts up with the antics of the young when they are very small, but he becomes less tolerant as they grow older and soon avoids them altogether.

(above)
Well known thieves in East African game parks, **black vervets** spend more time on the ground than other guenons. At such times they are more wary, and young babies cling to their mothers.

(below)
Chimpanzees are the most intelligent of the primates, with the exception of man. Great imitators, they can make an exciting variety of sounds and facial expressions and, recently, have been taught to communicate by sign language.

strange animals, back to Europe. The monkeys were regarded with a natural interest and curiosity because of their more obvious manlike qualities. Soon it was discovered that many could be taught to perform tricks. Up until a few years ago an organ-grinder with his monkey was a familiar sight on streets in America and Europe; and captive monkeys have always been among the most popular exhibits in every large zoo.

In the nineteenth century, Charles Darwin's theory of evolution created a new concept of the primates. Suddenly they became much more than interesting animals with bodies something like a human's. They were recognized as creatures with which man shared a common ancestry. From this new biological viewpoint studies of man's relations were seen to be useful in learning about the biology of man himself, and medical science began to take a new interest in the primates. The actions of monkeys and apes, and even of the less manlike prosimians, ceased to seem merely amusing when it was realized they could shed light on human actions. Psychologists have now used monkeys and apes for many years to study learning ability in the laboratory; but it is only in the last few years that another branch of study, called ethology, has begun in earnest to examine the patterns of conduct of primates in the wild. Most of these new studies are being undertaken in order to learn about the primates for their own sake; but a great deal of what is being discovered may some day help to explain the things that man himself does.

Primates have been put to even more practical uses. Rhesus monkeys are valuable in medical studies, chiefly because they have been easy to obtain and to keep in laboratories. From the rhesus monkey came the important discovery of the Rh, or rhesus, factor in the blood. Polio and other vaccines were first used on the rhesus monkeys, and at least one kind is made from the blood of immunized monkeys. Some of the first living creatures to travel through space were monkeys and chimpanzees, sent aloft to test the safety of systems designed for the ultimate use of man. In other places man has made less spectacular and less far-reaching uses of his kin. The skins of monkeys are made into ceremonial robes in parts of Africa, and elsewhere primitive tribes use monkeys as an item of diet.

It is a tragic fact that many species of primate that have contributed so much to man's welfare and knowledge are now facing possible extinction. The danger comes in many forms and for many reasons. First, the unchecked increase in human population means that people must occupy or cultivate increasing amounts of land; this inevitably means loss of living space for other creatures. A rare kind of colobus monkey from Zanzibar will become extinct as the trees in which it must live are cut down to clear the forest for agriculture. Other colobus monkeys are endangered by the current fad for rugs made of their skins. Squirrel monkeys from tropical America are being captured and imported into

(left)
For every **orangutan** delivered safely to a zoo, eight have died. Adults have been killed to capture babies. Babies have died from poor care. The animals have often been illegally caught and smuggled out of Sumatra and Borneo. Happily, zoos have recently agreed to take only those animals legally captured.

(below)
The beautiful **Diana monkey** is named after the goddess of the moon because of the crescent on its brow.

the United States for sale in pet shops in such quantities that this species may be in trouble. Not only do large numbers of the monkeys die of poor care before they reach the pet shops, but a great many die later because most of their purchasers are unaware of how much attention the animals need. Those monkeys that are sacrificed for medical-research purposes and for vaccine production die in a good cause; but even the best of causes cannot be forgiven if it does not take care to avoid the total extinction of the species it uses.

There is a glimmer of hope now that our lower relations will survive for future human generations to know and enjoy. A start has been made to halt the threat to certain species. Not long ago zoo people discovered that for every orangutan they bought, about eight other orangutans died. Adults were killed in capturing the babies and babies died of inadequate care by their captors. Most of the orangutans bought for zoos turned out to have been captured illegally, and smuggled out of their homelands. When the zoos learned these facts they agreed among themselves that even though they wanted the animals very badly they would buy none that was captured illegally. It is still too soon to be certain, but it looks as though this zoo boycott is making the illegal trade in orangutans unprofitable, and the species may now have a chance to survive. Too, zoos are intensifying their efforts to breed these rare animals, and so cut down the need to capture wild ones.

Medical researchers, realizing that the supply of monkeys is not limitless, are becoming interested in the conservation of wild populations. But in the long run the future of primates, as of all of the world's wild animals, will depend not solely on the actions of scientists. Whether the fascinating creatures which have shared the Earth with man over thousands of years will be allowed to continue to share it with him depends upon the actions of mankind as a whole. The wild animal species are, in a real sense, the lesser brothers of man, and man must be his brother's keeper.

► *There are a surprising number of strange creatures on this planet which are known mostly to zoologists.*

Little-Known Mammals

Mammals, the dominant form of animal life on earth today, have evolved over millions of years into countless strange forms and have developed a wide range of ways of life. Nevertheless all share in a few common characteristics: their bodies are clothed in a covering of hair at some stage of their development; they all breathe air; they feed their young with milk from mammary glands (whence the word "mammal" is derived); and they have a body temperature that is more or less independent of the temperature of the air or water in which they live.

Most of us are familiar with the larger, more spectacular species of the world, and with some of the commoner small ones of our region. Still, there is a surprising number of mammals found on this planet which are known only to zoologists. If you have heard of the wambenger, the cuscus or the angwantibo you are unusually familiar with the animal kingdom; if not, you will meet them in the pages that follow. Perhaps you are familiar with at least some of the animals in this book. If you are, your knowledge of the mammals is above average. See how many are new to you.

An Animal Without a Name

When an animal of a new species is discovered, a zoologist must write a detailed description of its appearance and make up a scientific name in Latin by which it will be officially designated; usually

A great number of strange animals exist that are little known to man. Many of them are rare or secretive; some move around only at night; others live in only partly explored regions or are isolated on islands. Unusual habits and appearance make all of them fascinating to study. One species of this **broad-footed phascogale** (above, right) has been seen running upside down on cave roofs. Pads on the bottoms of the hands and feet have ridges that aid the animal in climbing trees and rocky places.

As savage as a wolverine, the cat-sized **Tasmanian devil** is usually a scavenger, but it will kill mice and snakes for food and fiercely attack much larger animals when cornered. Though once common in Australia, it is now extinct there.

One of the rarest of mammals, the **black-shouldered opossum** is a South American marsupial that roams the trees at night and, like other opossums, will eat almost anything it can find.

it already has a common name, given to it by the inhabitants of the region in which it occurs. In the remote region of Cuzco, in southern Peru, a man who had spent much of his life there collecting animal specimens for museums, as his father had done before him since well before the turn of the century, came upon a kind of opossum he had never seen before. In fact it seems that no one had ever seen such an opossum, and when it reached the museum it was given the imposing scientific name, *Caluromysiops irrupta*. A second specimen was caught not long afterward. For eleven years the two specimens remained in the museum, of interest only to scientists, and no need for a common name in English arose.

Then, in 1961, one of these strange mammals arrived, in a shipment of Peruvian mammals, at the Bronx Zoo in New York City. Once the opossum was identified the zoo was faced with the necessity to find a common name to put on its label, along with the scientific one; since no such name existed, the zoo coined the name "black-shouldered opossum". With its beautiful pearl-grey fur, black markings and ears of apricot hue, this is the handsomest of New World marsupials. Its habits, unknown in the wild, are very similar in the zoo to those of the much more common, and closely related, woolly opossum. Both are nocturnal, omnivorous (feeding on both animal and vegetable substance) and at home among the branches of trees.

A Case of Mistaken Identity

THE FIRST SKIN of a yapok sent to a museum in Europe over 150 years ago was thought to belong to a pigmy species of otter, for it had a dense, waterproof fur and webbed hind feet. However when a skull became available for examination, the animal was found to be an opossum, and a very odd one at that. Not even in Australia, where marsupials evolved into "copies" of mice, badgers and wolves, have any ever taken to an aquatic life, and the yapok stands alone in this respect. From southern Mexico to northern Argentina, in lakes and streams, even in those high in the mountains, yapoks can be found. However they do not seem to be common anywhere, and their nocturnal habits often allow them to go unnoticed. Their smoky-grey fur, with broad crossbands of black, is distinctive.

The yapok's way of swimming at the surface of the water is unusual, too. Such mammals as muskrats and otters, which propel themselves principally by means of their hind feet, fold their forepaws against the chest at such times, but the yapok holds its arms stiffly out under the water, unwebbed fingers extended, and seems to steer itself, at least partially, by changing the angle at which the hands and arms are held. In the wild, yapoks are believed to eat fish and crayfish, and in the zoo they hold a small fish in one hand and eat from one end until it is finished.

A "Devil" with a Pouch

THE TASMANIAN DEVIL is not a very pretty animal to look at, with its bear-shaped body and a head that seems to have been meant for an animal half again as large. The devil belongs to the large and varied family of marsupials called dasyurids, which also contains the agile, predatory "native cats" and marsupial "mice". Although ill-tempered and a fierce fighter when cornered, the devil prefers to be a scavenger, like the hyena, devouring the leftovers of kills made by other predators. Still it can and does occasionally kill for itself—small mammals, ground-nesting birds and even snakes.

The pouch of a female Tasmanian devil is not very large, and her

(bottom left)
Unlike other opossums, the **yapok** is semiaquatic and dives for fish and shellfish. It swims underwater by holding its arms stiffly out, changing the angle of the arms and hands to steer while using its webbed feet for propulsion.

(below)
Capable of tremendous leaps, the **flying phalanger** of Australia has flaps of skin under its arms similar to those of a flying squirrel. It uses these flaps as a parachute, half-gliding to the next tree.

CHADER

two or three young quickly outgrow it; she then makes a nest of leaves or grass in which she leaves the babies while she is out seeking food. The devil makes its home underground—often in an unused wombat burrow—in the thick scrub growth of its native island of Tasmania.

The "Mouse" That Isn't

THE SAME FAMILY that gave rise to the Tasmanian devil has also produced a number of smaller creatures called marsupial "mice". Quick and active, the marsupial "mice" behave more like shrews, running down and eating insects for the most part, although they are known to take mice and other small vertebrates as well. Generally nocturnal, they construct nests of grass and leaves in burrows underground or under logs and stumps. The fat-tailed marsupial mouse normally moves about on all four feet, but when in a hurry can hop quite well using its hind feet alone.

The Would-be Dormice

LOOKING VERY MUCH LIKE the true rodent dormice they emulate in their actions, the pigmy possums of the Australian region have undertaken a form of "hibernation" which resembles that of the true dormice, except in timing. For the pigmy possum does not confine its deep slumber to winter, and in fact may awaken even in cold weather to hunt for food. When food is plentiful the tiny possum stores fat in its thick tail; it draws upon this fat during its torpid periods. Pigmy possums have been observed to eat insects and spiders, and even small lizards, and some zoologists have seen them eat flower petals in captivity.

A snug nest of shredded bark serves as a home by day and during cold weather, but occasionally one is more adventurous. One zoologist has over the years captured several that entered his tent and dozed off in comfort in his sleeping bag. Often two or more pigmy possums will sleep in the same nest, each curled tightly into a ball.

(right)
Because of its small size, the **wambenger,** or red-tailed phalanger, is preyed upon by many larger animals, particularly those that have been introduced into Australia such as dogs, cats and foxes.

(far right)
Like dormice, the primitive **pigmy opossum** hibernates part of the year, after storing ample fat in its body and in its tail, which sometimes becomes quite bulbous.

Although sluggish in movement, the **cuscus** of Australia is similar in habits to the South American kinkajous. It is a nocturnal tree-dweller that feeds on vegetation, insects and small animals. Its unusual prehensile tail is partially covered with rasping, pointed scales.

A Cuscus Takes Its Time

EXCEPT FOR ITS PLODDING WAYS and its hue, the slow-moving cuscus of New Guinea is reminiscent of the South American kinkajou. It is nocturnal, and its grasping paws and prehensile tail are perfect for a life spent mostly up in trees. It even eats much the same sort of things the kinkajou does—vegetation, fruits, insects and small vertebrates. But where the kinkajou is agile and quick in its movements, the cuscus is not.

Female cuscuses are more or less uniformly brownish grey, but the males appear to be a yellowish white with irregular dark spots on the back. Actually, the dark tone of the male is its basic body hue, while the white has grown so extensive that it has all but obliterated the original hue. It may seem silly to ponder whether an animal is white with dark spots or dark covered with white, but the answers to such questions often throw light upon the evolutionary history of a species.

The Wondrous Wambenger

NO OTHER PEOPLE of the world have applied to their native animals so many wonderful-sounding names as have the Australians, but then no other continent has so many animals to which ordinary names would hardly seem appropriate. The little marsupial called the red-tailed phascogale (from its scientific name) or more prosaically, one of the brush-tailed marsupial rats, seems somehow more wondrous when spoken of by its alternate name, "wambenger".

A chipmunk-sized inhabitant of southern Australia, this nocturnal tree climber sports a tail clothed in short red hair for about half its length, ending in a thick, brushy tip. It lives upon insects, and is in turn preyed upon by larger animals. The first specimen known to science, in fact, was killed and brought home in the early part of the nineteenth century by a house cat. Unfortunately, such imported animals as cats, dogs and foxes have continued over the years to kill the comparatively unintelligent native mammals of Australia, until many of them are now quite rare.

Kangaroos with Wrap-around Tails

THE RAT-KANGAROOS, small cousins of the familiar kangaroos, are generally unknown outside of Australia, except to zoologists. No larger than a small rabbit, and only vaguely kangaroo-shaped, their solitary way of life and their nocturnal habits have kept them out of the limelight. The numerous species of rat-kangaroos differ in appearance, but behave in much the same way. Like their large relatives they are strict vegetarians, eating mainly grass, but including on the menu such other items as fungi that grow underground and tubers similar to yams.

Unlike the big kangaroos, these diminutive 'roos have prehensile tails which they wrap tightly around nest material to transport it to the nesting site. They differ from most of the large kangaroos, too, in being very antisocial. Two of the more different-looking species are the brush-tailed rat-kangaroo and the long-nosed rat-kangaroo.

A Nose Full of Fingers

THE STAR-NOSED MOLE of eastern North America is unique among mammals, bearing at the tip of its snout a flower-like structure of twenty-two pink, fleshy "tentacles". These sensitive projections are organs of touch, useful in detecting the many small insects that form its diet, either in its tunnels or along the bottoms of streams and ponds, where it often hunts. It is known, too, to eat small fish from time to time. The star-nosed mole is a good swimmer, and usually digs its burrows in wet places.

It is seen above ground more often than other moles, both by day and by night. In late spring the female gives birth to a litter of from three to six young, which are hairless and blind, with fleshy nose-stars that are short and stumpy. By the time the young are three weeks old, however, they have grown thick coats of dense fur, and are ready to leave their mother to live on their own.

A Prickly Ball

ONE OF THE MORE COMMON of Madagascar's strange mammals is the small hedgehog-tenrec, a relative of the shrews and the true hedgehogs. Highly insectivorous, the hedgehog-tenrec waddles with a

Because of the remoteness of its habitat in the Congo rain forest and its protective coloration—a purplish-brown hide over most of its body and a unique, zebra-like pattern of stripes on its rump—few non-Africans have ever seen an **okapi** in the wild. For these same reasons, it wasn't until 1901 that this animal was discovered by science. It is a relative of the giraffe and can run with surprising speed through the tangles of vines and branches of its home territory. The okapi also has very keen hearing, as indicated by its large ears. Pygmies and leopards are its chief predators.

(right)
Sole survivor of an ancient group of primates, the **tarsier** has enormous eyes for seeing in the dark and a long tail used for balancing itself. Its fingers and toes end in rounded, adhesive pads similar to the discs on the feet of tree frogs, which aid in holding on to branches.

(far right)
When enemies threaten, the **hedgehog-tenrec,** a small insectivore from Madagascar, rolls up in a tight ball like a true hedgehog, protecting its soft underside and showing only the sharp spines that cover its back.

clumsy gait along the ground and climbs slowly but effectively among the branches of shrubs in search of insects, which it minces into tiny fragments with its small, sharp teeth. When danger threatens the hedgehog-tenrec, like a true hedgehog it rolls up into a tight ball, presenting only a surface of sharp spines to any would-be attacker and keeping its soft underside, which has no spines, safely in the center of the ball. The hedgehog-tenrec is active only at night, and goes into a deep sleep during the Madagascar winter.

The Mango Planter

Bats are the only mammals that have achieved true flight (as distinguished from the gliding of "flying" squirrels and some others), and their mastery of the air has given them the freedom to experiment with a variety of ways of life. Most bats prefer a diet of insects, but some have become fishermen, others are highly carnivorous, and some, the vampires, drink the blood from living animals. Two groups of bats have taken to a diet of fruit. One of these groups contains the largest of all bats, the flying foxes of Asia.

In Africa are found smaller cousins of the flying foxes, the epaulet bats, although with a twenty-inch wing span they are small only in a relative sense. By day the epaulet bat hangs from the limb of a tree, often in company with several dozen others, its leathery wings wrapped around it like a cloak. At night it leaves the roost to fly off in search of such fruits as bananas, figs and mangoes, and it has been credited with introducing the mango into new areas from undigested seeds which it drops in flight.

The Goblin of the Islands

A tarsier's face seems to be all eyes, and indeed, the eye sockets in its skull are by far its most prominent feature. The tarsier, native to a number of islands which trail southward and eastward from the Malay peninsula, looks like a spindly version of the African bush-babies; its way of life, as it happens, is in many respects similar to theirs. The tarsier moves about by hopping many feet from branch to branch, using its long tail for balance and grasping its new perch with long, pad-tipped fingers and toes. Like the bushbabies, the tarsier is nocturnal, but unlike them it seems to eat no plant material at all. Constantly alert, its large eyes peering intently and its ears moving ceaselessly to catch the sound of an insect or an enemy, the tarsier is instantly ready to move like a wraith, toward a meal or toward safety.

Softly-softlies, Angwantibos and Bushbabies

AMONG THE PRIMATES, the loris family contains perhaps the oddest assortment of species, whose two main branches in Africa scarcely resemble each other at all. Like the true lorises of Asia, the potto and angwantibo of Africa are creatures of deliberate movement, which progress carefully along the limbs of trees on all four feet. The second branch of the family, the bushbabies, are lightly-built acrobats, quick of movement, and fond of leaping from branch to branch as if they were tiny kangaroos. Two habits are shared by both groups, however: all of the species are forest dwellers and all dine on the same basic bill of fare—insects, small vertebrates and plant material. In addition, all are nocturnal.

The slow-moving potto hardly ever seems to be in a hurry. In fact its slow, almost delicate way of walking has earned the potto the native name, softly-softly. Even when it is pursuing living prey, it picks its way carefully, its only quick movements being a fast snatch with its hands at the last moment. When threatened it can bite suddenly and savagely, but at other times the potto spurns haste. It is admirably adapted for its slow life high in the forest; short-limbed and stocky, it lacks the long tail that is characteristic of animals which move quickly in the forest canopy. Long tails are balancing organs, used like a tight-rope walker's pole. The potto, because it moves slowly, firmly grasping each branch with its peculiar hands and feet, can do nicely with a short, stubby tail.

Like a human thumb, the potto's thumb and great toe are opposable to the other digits to provide a firm grasp. Its index fingers are mere nubbins, and the second toes are also shortened. The spines of the vertebrae in the potto's neck are particularly long and sometimes pro-trude through the skin. When threatened the potto tucks its head between its arms, exposing the back of its neck. If a predator comes too close, the potto rams it with its neck, and it is said that the verte-bral spines serve as a defensive weapon. The potto's teeth, however, are still its most effective protection, and the tenacity of its bite has given rise to the African legend that a biting potto will not relax its hold until sundown.

Slow-moving and vulnerable, the **potto** protects itself by tucking its head between its front legs, exposing sharp spines on the back of its neck. These can be used for butting the enemy.

Much rarer than the potto is its smaller cousin the angwantibo, sometimes called the golden potto. Twelve inches long, about two-thirds the size of the potto, the angwantibo differs from it in a number of ways. The angwantibo's longer snout gives its face a rather fox-like appearance. At the other extreme, its tail is so short that it lies hidden under the animal's short, woolly hair. The golden potto's limbs are more slender and longer, and unlike the potto, it often moves about nimbly. When threatened, the angwantibo assumes the potto's defen-

(right)
Although somewhat different in appearance, the agile bushbabies and the slow-moving pottos belong to the same group of animals that diverged long ago from the main lemur and primate line.

(below)
A rare cousin of the potto, the **angwantibo** is two-thirds its size with smaller eyes and a pointed, foxlike nose. Like the potto, it is nocturnal and, during the day, it will often sleep hanging from a branch, gripping it very tightly.

CONGO POTTO

MOHOLI BUSHBABY

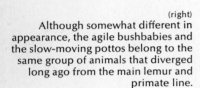

PIGMY BUSHBABY

A full, silky mane gives the **golden marmoset** the look of a little lion, but its habits, such as scampering and jumping through the trees, are like those of other marmosets. The father marmoset takes over the duties of caring for the young.

sive posture, even ramming an enemy with its neck, but it does not have the potto's peculiar vertebral armament. Like a potto the angwantibo sometimes sleeps hunched over, but both often sleep hanging from a branch with a grip so tight that there is little chance of an accidental slip.

The bushbabies, or galagos, are the acrobats of the family. One species grows to be larger than a potto, but the other kinds are squirrel-sized or smaller. Most kinds are gregarious and they are seen more often in small groups than singly. Most common of the bushbabies, both in the wild and in zoos, is the Moholi bushbaby, whose large soft brown eyes and kitten-like face make it a most appealing creature. Although it does eat fruits, insects seem to form a major part of the little primate's diet; a bound and a lightning-fast grab of the long-fingered hands, and the bushbaby has its choice morsel, which it begins to eat with its eyes closed, to protect them from possible injury by the insect's flailing feet. Bushbabies do not travel widely, and mark their territories with urine, applied carefully to branches.

The pigmy bushbaby, not much larger than a large mouse, is the smallest of the family, but its voice is probably by far the most powerful. Anyone hearing for the first time its call, a ringing chatter reminiscent of hysterical laughter, would find it difficult to believe that an animal so tiny could be its source. Its habits, so far as they are known, seem to be much like those of the Moholi bushbaby.

Mother's Helper

THOSE SMALLEST NEW WORLD primates, the marmosets, come in a variety of hues, ranging from black through brown and red and yellow to white. Most of the species live in the vast Amazon Basin of

The enormous, owl-like eyes of the **douroucouli,** a South American monkey, are well adapted for its night habits. It is the only nocturnal monkey.

South America, but some range as far north as Panama. Among the most striking of the group is the golden or lion-maned marmoset of eastern Brazil. Clothed in a silky coat of orange-yellow, topped by a large ruff of hair on the sides and back of the head, it does remind one of a lion. But in action it is all marmoset, scampering and leaping in the trees in small bands, pouncing upon insects and small vertebrates with quick movements, and eating them with gusto. As is common in all marmosets, the father golden marmoset carries his one or two babies around with him, relieving his mate of the usual primate's maternal chores, and returning them to her to nurse. In a year the babies reach full size and are no longer dependent upon their parents, but often the father continues to watch out for them.

Monkeys in Capes

Sakis are odd monkeys, also found in the Amazon Basin. A long cape of glossy dark hair covers a saki's body and makes it appear to be much larger than it actually is; under its robust exterior the saki has a spindly, long-limbed body that seems to have just enough flesh over the bones to hold them together. Still, the saki is far from frail, and often makes great leaps from one branch to another. It eats a variety of foods—fruits, flowers and leaves, and small animals—and there is even a report of a group of the monkeys plucking sleeping bats from a hollow tree, tearing them apart by hand and eating them. Sakis are rarely seen in zoos, for they do not usually do well in captivity.

A Nocturnal Monkey

Although the lower primates (tarsiers, pottos, bushbabies, etc.) have almost all adopted the night as their active time, the monkeys have chosen to spend the night asleep and to go about the business of making a living under the sun. One monkey is an exception; the douroucouli, or, as it is sometimes called, night monkey, sleeps away the hours of sunlight while its near relatives are abroad. Its eyes, which

(bottom left)
A long-haired monkey of South America, the **bearded saki,** or Humboldt's saki, grows a beard from its cheeks and chin similar to the beard of a man.

(bottom right)
Rarely seen in zoos, the **sakiwinki** does poorly in captivity. Its enormous vocabulary, with special alarm calls, can be heard for miles.

are large for a monkey, serve it well in the dimness of the night-time forest, as it leaps and scampers nimbly in pursuit of insects and small vertebrates, or searches for fruits among the leaves. From Central America through the northern part of South America the douroucouli fills the darkened forest with a variety of calls, as individuals meet or maintain contact in the darkness.

The Toothless Tree-dweller

THE TAMANDUA of Central and South America seeks out both on the ground and in trees the ants and termites that are its food. On the ground its method of feeding, which is similar to that of its larger, strictly terrestrial cousin, the giant anteater, consists of tearing open ant and termite nests with its large, stout and sharp claws, and lapping up its prey with a long, sticky tongue. However, unlike the giant anteater, which walks on its knuckles to protect the sharpness of its claws, the tamandua walks on the outer sides of its forepaws, turning its claws inward to protect them. Up in a tree the tamandua tears open the nests of arboreal termites and ants in much the same way as on the forest floor, except that it anchors itself firmly by wrapping its prehensile tail around the limb on which it is standing. Were the tamandua not to do this, the force it needs to rip through the tough nests might throw it off balance. The tamandua's single offspring rides upon its mother's back until it is old enough to get around by itself.

The Sleepers

THE COMMON DORMOUSE of Europe was introduced into England by the Romans, for reasons best explained by another of its names, "edible dormouse"; its reputation as a delicacy seems to have fallen into general disuse today, however. A pleasant, if infrequently seen inhabitant of woodlands and gardens, the small rodent looks and acts like a squirrel, eating the same foods, but it is active only by night. During the fall the dormouse eats a great deal and stores up a heavy

Like the larger species of dormice, the **hazel mouse** hibernates in the winter, curled up in a snug nest woven of plant materials, and awakens occasionally to eat nuts it has stored away.

Although agile on the ground, the **tamandua** spends a great deal of its time in trees, feeding on termites and ants that make their nests on branches or creepers. Its long, sharp claws are used for tearing open the nests, while the long prehensile tail is wrapped around a branch to prevent falling.

A very rare rodent, the **pacarana** of South America is a mild-mannered vegetarian with a high-pitched, cooing call that changes to a growl when the animal is angry.

layer of fat for the winter. It also stores such things as nuts and may awaken from its hibernation from time to time for a snack, only to return to deep torpor in a snug nest woven of plant materials. The hazel mouse, a smaller species, and an original inhabitant of England as well as Europe, has very similar habits.

Too Much of a Good Thing

THE LEMMINGS ARE SMALL RODENTS of the arctic regions that have been said, inaccurately, to commit suicide en masse every few years. Suicide, however, is the farthest thing from the lemmings' intention at such times; in years of plentiful food the little rodents prosper and produce more young than usual. Over a period of several years the lemming population increases steadily, until the food supply cannot keep up with them, and the increased social pressures of meeting too many other lemmings in an overcrowded area drives large numbers of them to seek living space elsewhere. The lemmings strike out for new land, swimming across streams and rivers, and even setting out to sea. During these emigrations vast numbers die, and at times their bodies are washed up to line the shore. When lemmings are abundant the predators that depend upon them, the snowy owl and lynx, for example, also increase in number, only to face their own food shortage when the lemming population suddenly declines.

The Bouncing Elf

WHAT WE TEND TO THINK OF as the kangaroo shape is by no means solely the possession of kangaroos. On every continent except Antarctica some small mammal groups have independently developed a hopping gait, and along with it the most efficient shape for hopping—long balancing tail, tiny forelegs and enormous hind feet. In the main these hopping mammals are inhabitants of open country, plains and deserts, and most of them are rat-sized or smaller.

(right)
Feeding on succulent desert vegetation, the **jerboa** never drinks water, but it manufactures its own from seeds and other plant life it eats.

(far right)
When food is abundant, the arctic **lemming** multiplies rapidly, until food shortages in overcrowded areas force vast numbers to migrate to new land. Thousands of these small rodents die by drowning or from various other causes during the migration, reducing the population to normal levels again.

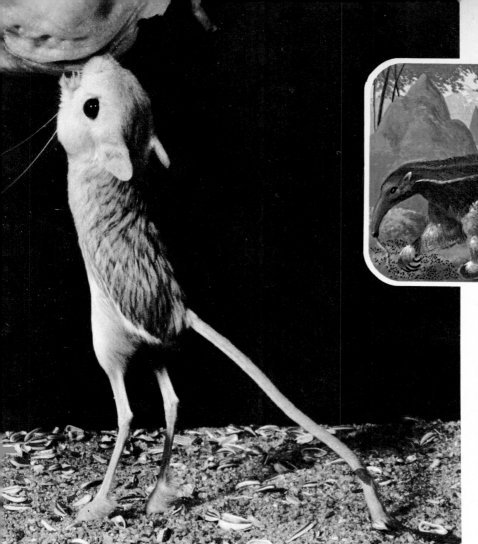

CHADER

(left)
Night creature of the deserts of North Africa, the **jerboa** can walk backwards or forwards, pace on its long, thin hind legs and jump as far as six feet, all with incredible speed.

(above)
An amazingly quick and deadly fighter, the **giant anteater** is seldom bothered by other animals. Its forearms have enormous muscles and the short, stout fingers are armed with gigantic claws. When attacked, it stands on its hind legs and lashes out with its claws in every direction.

One of these is the desert jerboa of northern Africa, a four-inch-long rodent with a tail as much as six inches in length. Jerboas spend the hot desert day sleeping in subterranean burrows where the temperature does not rise too high; they are not solitary, as so many desert animals are, and several may share the same nest. Nightfall finds the jerboa above ground again, foraging for seeds and such vegetation as the desert affords. As far as is known the jerboa, like some other desert rodents, never drinks water, but manufactures it metabolically from the plant material it eats. When in a hurry a jerboa can cover six feet or more in a single bound.

Something Like a Rabbit

THERE ARE NO RABBITS or hares on the arid, wind-scoured Patagonian Plateau of Argentina, but there ought to be, for apart from its constant winds, the terrain resembles in many ways the kind of country that supports jackrabbits in North America. And as so often happens in nature, another mammal group, in this case the cavy family of rodents, has produced a species that lives like a rabbit and has something of the same appearance. The Patagonian cavy, or mara, does not carry the physical resemblance too far, however; it has short ears and runs, rather than bounds, as a rabbit would. The Patagonian cavy lives in small groups, occasionally up to several dozen in number. It digs a shallow burrow, sometimes modifying an existing one made by some other animal, but is often seen sitting on its haunches or lying out in the sun. Its food consists of grasses and other kinds of plants. To see this long-legged, rabbit-like creature one would hardly suspect that its closest living relatives are the chunky little guinea pigs.

The Terrible Mouse

THE PACARANA, whose scientific name, *Dinomys,* means "terrible mouse", is an inoffensive rodent which dwells along the base of the northern Andes Mountains in South America. Although it reminds one of a large woodchuck with an overgrown head, the pacarana actually belongs to the large subdivision of rodents characterized by the porcupines. Pacaranas are mild-mannered vegetarians, apparently rather dull-witted, and docile in captivity. They seem nowhere to be really common, but are sometimes captured by the natives to be eaten or kept as pets. When annoyed the pacarana utters a low growl, and at other times may make a high-pitched, plaintive cooing sound.

Little Cousins of the Bears

SO CLOSELY IS THE RACCOON family related to the bear family that over the years one species, the giant panda, has been considered alternately by zoologists to belong to one or the other family. The members of the raccoon family, kinkajou, coati, cacomistle and raccoon, to name the most familiar, do not show their kinship to the bears externally, and for that matter, except for the ringed tail that all but the kinkajou have, they even bear little resemblance to one another. The pandas, giant and lesser, are native to eastern Asia, and all of the remaining species live in the New World. The raccoon is a common and well-known inhabitant of much of North America, and one of the few mammals to hold its own against the encroachments of suburban civilization. It has a delicate sense of touch in its forepaws, which it uses to feel in streamside mud for the small living things which make up a part of its diet. A second species of raccoon ranges through northern South America, as far north as Panama.

Three species of coati are found in the Americas, from the southwestern United States through much of South America. They are lighter

Quite common but seldom seen, the **cacomistle,** a relative of the raccoon, is nocturnal and can squeeze into extremely narrow cracks and crevices. It is native to the southwestern United States and to Central America.

CACOMISTLE

(above)
Although one of the rarest of the large mammals, the **giant panda** of China is well known because of the publicity given to specimens in American and European zoos. Attempts made to breed these animals in captivity have so far been unsuccessful.

(right)
Patagonian counterparts of the North American jack rabbit, **maras** can often be seen in small groups, sitting on their haunches beside shallow burrows on the dry pampas grass.

(below)
A rugged rodent of the South American forests, the **paca** roams about at night digging huge holes, gnawing through large roots and eating practically anything it can find.

RACCOON

COATI

in build than the raccoon, with long snouts and long, thin tails which they usually carry upright as they walk. Coatis are active day and night, unlike the largely nocturnal raccoon, but their appetites include the same wide range of small vertebrates, invertebrates and plants.

Tropical forests, from southern Mexico through Brazil, provide a home for the kinkajou, a golden-brown, almost monkey-like member of the family. The kinkajou spends most of its time in the trees, where it makes excellent use of its prehensile tail. Although it does not disdain insects and other small living food, the kinkajou much prefers fruits, which form the bulk of its diet. The kinkajou's smaller cousin, the olingo, resembles it closely, except that its tail is not prehensile and has a faint marking of dark rings. The olingo's muzzle is more pointed than the kinkajou's, and resembles that of the cacomistle, the last member of the family that we will consider here.

The cacomistle, cacomixtle, ring-tailed cat, or just plain "ringtail", ranges through western North America from Oregon to southern Mexico. Not a cat, its habits are so cat-like that the mistaken name is forgivable; indeed, miners in the old West often kept a tame cacomistle in their cabins to rid them of mice and rats, for it is much more carnivorous than the other members of the family. This practice is still carried on occasionally today, but at least one owner of a curio shop had unexpected and unpleasant results. He liberated a pair of cacomistles in his shop to kill the packrats that carried off his souvenirs when the shop was closed for the winter. The cacomistles did eliminate the packrats, but were far more playful than anticipated and in a few days broke all of the items they were meant to protect.

The Red Fox on Stilts

THE GRASSLANDS OF SOUTH AMERICA are the home of one of the most unusual—and certainly the tallest—members of the dog family. The maned wolf, which is not a wolf in any sense of the word, is

(below)
Readily eating any animal they can catch, **kinkajous** also relish fruits, green nuts, leaves, fungi and honey.

(bottom)
One of the few animals known to use tools, the **sea otter** places a shellfish on its chest and pounds it repeatedly with a stone until the shell cracks.

SEA OTTER

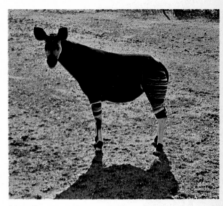

(left)
Almost hunted to extinction for its fine fur, the **sea otter** is now protected by international law, and the Pacific herds are gradually increasing.

(above)
A forest-dwelling relative of the giraffe, the **okapi** was not even discovered until this century. Inhabiting the Ituri Forest of the Congo, it is a browser and uses its long, prehensile tongue to grab and pull down leaves.

rather a close kin of the foxes, and its appearance substantiates the relationship. The reddish fur and black legs, which give rise to the description, "a red fox on stilts", are probably merely coincidental, but the long-snouted, almost delicate face of the maned wolf are a legacy from its fox-like ancestors.

Nor is the animal wolf-like in its actions. It does not run in packs, but lives a solitary life as a rule, and has never been known to attack man. Almost nothing is known of the habits of the maned wolf in the wild, so wary is it of man's approach, but in captivity it is very fond of fruit and meat. An occasional sheep killing has been blamed on it, but the bulk of meat in the maned wolf's diet doubtless comes from small rodents, such as mice and agoutis, and other vertebrates of small size. A short mane of hair that can be erected has given the maned wolf its English name, but it is one of its local, native names, Azuara-Guazu, that really evokes the mystery which still surrounds this strangest of the wild dogs.

The Supine Mariner

WHEN ONE BRANCH of the weasel family took to the water and developed into the otters, it spread over almost all of the world, except for the Australian region. All of its members chose fresh water, except for two species. One, a kind of fresh-water otter of South America, has only recently taken to living offshore along the coast of Chile; the other species, the sea otter, took to the sea in the North Pacific Ocean so long ago that its form and habits have changed greatly from those of its river-inhabiting cousins. Shorter-tailed, it has hind feet so large that they resemble flippers and make travel on land awkward.

While most animals prefer to live "right-side up", the sea otter spends most of its time floating on its back. In this position it sleeps and eats, using its chest as a table. In fact, when the sea otter brings up a mussel from the ocean floor, it also brings up a small stone, which it rests on its chest. Then, holding the mussel in its forepaws, it strikes

(top left)
In spite of its large, doglike claws, the **tayra,** a South American marten, can almost gallop through the trees after small prey.

(top right)
Looking like a cross between a bear and a raccoon, the **lesser panda** lives in holes in trees, but it spends much time foraging on the ground.

(below)
A fearsome carnivore for its size, the **marten** runs swiftly along branches in pursuit of squirrels, birds and mice. When food is scarce, martens will feed on kills made by other animals or raid barnyards to steal poultry.

the shellfish repeatedly against the stone, to break the shell and make the flesh available. Apart from the chimpanzee, the sea otter is the only mammal known to use any object as a tool to accomplish a task it could not otherwise do by itself. Where it is not disturbed by man the sea otter comes up on shoreline rocks to sleep at night, but elsewhere it anchors itself by wrapping strands of kelp around its body, and spends the night afloat, sleeping on its back.

A Sweet Tooth

THE YELLOW-THROATED MARTEN is one of the most handsome of the weasel family, a denizen of the forests from India to China and South-east Asia. It is found in both tropical growth and in the trees that grow on the slopes of the Himalaya Mountains. Active and agile, the marten races in pursuit of such nimble prey as squirrels and birds on the forest floor and with equal ease among the treetops. In fact, like the other species of martens that occupy the northern regions of Eurasia and North America, the yellow-throated marten prefers to hunt high above the ground. Animals are not the only item on its menu, however, and it is known to be fond of the nectar of certain flowers, pushing its pointed muzzle into the blooms to lap up the sweet fluid. When hunting is poor, the marten will content itself with eating the remains of kills made by other animals.

The Vanishing Hunter

A HUNDRED YEARS AGO the black-footed ferret was almost as familiar a sight on the Great Plains of North America as the prairie dog. Indeed, the ferret was found only where there were prairie dog villages, because it relied upon these large ground squirrels for both food and shelter. Able to descend into the prairie dogs' burrows, because of its trim shape, the ferret came to prey so heavily upon them that as agriculture destroyed the vast, sprawling prairie dog colonies the black-footed ferret began to disappear, too, until today it is among the rarest of North American mammals. Why the ferret began to vanish with the dogs is not easy to say, for it was known to eat other rodents as well. Nevertheless it *is* gone from much of its former range, and is not abundant even where it does occur.

The Gypsy Mongoose

To most persons the name "mongoose" conjures up an image of a long, lithe cobra-killer, the Indian mongoose. That species, however, is only one of a large number of kinds of mongoose, most of which are found not in Asia but in Africa. The smallest of the African species is the dwarf mongoose, a rather short but trim creature with a stubby snout. The dwarf mongoose prefers the company of its fellows, living in bands of up to a dozen or so. As far as anyone knows it has no permanent home, and the band leads a gypsy life, wandering widely by day, foraging for whatever items of its broad diet it can discover (insects, small vertebrates, eggs and fruits are all on the bill of fare). At nightfall the little mongooses move into any convenient shelter, often sleeping in the tunnels of deserted termite mounds.

A Shaggy Mass of Hair

A sleeping binturong looks for all the world like a large unkempt mass of black horsehair, and when it awakens it is not much different, except for its small bear-like face that wears a permanently bewildered expression. The binturong is the largest member of the civet family, but while most of the civets are active predators the binturong appears to dine mainly on fruits and other vegetation; it is the only member of the family—and one of the few mammals outside of the New World tropics—that has a prehensile tail. Trees are the binturong's

(above)
Living in bands of up to a dozen, the **dwarf mongoose** leads a gypsy life, wandering by day in search of insects, small vertebrates, eggs and fruit. At night, it sometimes sleeps in deserted termite mounds.

(left)
Now one of the rarest of North American mammals, the **black-footed ferret** was once abundant throughout the Great Plains. When man started poisoning the prairie dog colonies to make way for agriculture, the ferret population also decreased, since it lived mainly on prairie dogs.

home, and it picks its way through them carefully and with deliberation, leaving to its cousins such more rapid means of locomotion as leaping. When taken young, binturongs often make docile pets, although their nocturnal habits and strong mousy scent do not count as assets.

A Versatile Carnivore

A MORE TYPICAL MEMBER of the civet family is the false palm civet of Africa, a carnivore which, like so many others, seems to prefer fruits as well as small animals. Cat-sized, it is clothed in short, woolly fur, usually smoky-brown liberally sprinkled with black spots, and partially ringed with black on the tail. A whitish spot on each shoulder is characteristic, but is sometimes so faint as to be easily missed. The palm civet is equally at home high in the canopy layer of the forest and on the floor, and is one of the commonest animals of the continent. In many parts of Africa palm civets are kept as household pets and generally remain tame, repaying their masters by killing rats and mice.

The Lurker on the Limb

M ANY PEOPLE CONSIDER the clouded leopard to be the most beautiful of all the cats. Not so large as the true leopard, it spends more time in trees, often lying motionless on a low-hanging limb, until some unsuspecting small herbivore passes beneath. Until that time the unusual

(bottom right)
An animal paradox, the Asian **binturong** is a rambling vegetarian related to the civets. Its face, growl and walk are more like those of a bear, and it is the only mammal outside Australia and South America that has a prehensile tail.

(below)
Civets are the source of an aromatic substance which is used as a fixative in perfumes. This substance is produced by the anal glands of the animal, and civets are often kept and "milked" regularly.

(left)
Unlike most cats, which ambush their prey, the long-legged **serval** runs down small game over short distances. It can catch birds on the wing by jumping into the air as high as six feet.

(below)
Possessing enormous fangs (proportionally larger than those of any other cat), the beautifully-marked **clouded leopard,** a secretive prowler of the Southeast Asian jungles, seems to feed mostly on birds and monkeys, though very little is known about its habits.

network pattern of the clouded leopard's coat provides an excellent camouflage; then the cat leaps down, dealing swift death with its enormous canine teeth, which are longer, in proportion to the clouded leopard's size, than in any other of the world's big cats.

Not all hunting is done from ambush above, for the clouded leopard also hunts on the ground. Much of its prey consists of small mammals and birds, from chevrotains to monkeys, but occasionally it is known to attack creatures as large as a buffalo calf. It is found throughout much of South-east Asia, from the islands of Sumatra and Borneo north into southern China.

A Tall Cat

THE SERVAL IS FOUND throughout most of Africa south of the Sahara Desert, generally in brushy or forested country. Long-necked and long-legged, with a black-spotted, golden-tan coat, it is an impressive member of the cat family. Whereas most of the world's cats hunt from ambush or by a stealthy approach until the last moment, the serval uses its long limbs to run down prey, over short distances at least, and is known to catch birds that it has put to flight by leaping high into the air after them. It is an adept climber, too, and can hunt in trees.

Suction Cups for Climbing

A LOUD, PIERCING SCREAM in the night is often the only indication a visitor to the forests of Africa has that there are tree hyraxes about. Nocturnal and at home high above the ground, the tree hyrax or dassie is not often seen as it goes about nibbling leaves and an occasional insect in the shadowy foliage.

Although it looks as if it were a rodent of some kind, the hyrax is more nearly related to the hoofed animals, from whose ancestors its

(right)
The forest-dwelling **tapir** prefers to stay close to water, eating tender vegetation and submerging up to its snout to escape bothersome insects.

(below)
When angry, the South American **collared peccary** will clap its jaws together as a warning to intruders that it is ready to attack. Peccaries can give severe bites.

forbears began to diverge in the far distant past. Its feet are peculiar; except for the second toe of the hind foot, each toe ends in a broad, hoof-like nail, and the soles of the feet are hairless pads kept moist by a glandular secretion and provided with muscles that pull in the middle of the pad, making the foot into a very effective suction cup for clinging to trees. Newborn hyraxes are nearly half as large as their mothers, and able to run about with them soon after birth.

The Scattered Clan

IN PREHISTORIC TIMES tapirs were found throughout much of the world, but today the last survivors of the group live in only two widely separated parts of the globe. Three species occur in the New World tropics from Mexico to Paraguay and Brazil, and a fourth species, the Malay tapir, inhabits South-east Asia and Sumatra. The tapirs of the New World are a uniform brownish grey, but the Malay tapir, blackish on the head, neck and legs, bears a white saddle over the rear three-quarters of its body. All young tapirs, however, are dark brown with rows of white stripes and spots running fore to aft, a pattern which, like the spotting of deer fawns, probably helps to camouflage them in the forest.

Tapirs are forest dwellers, but prefer to stay in the close vicinity of water, where they can submerge to escape insects, and where they find succulent aquatic vegetation. Adult tapirs have few enemies, outside of man, except the jaguar in the New World and the tiger in Asia, but many of the smaller carnivores probably pose a threat to very young ones. Still, throughout their range, tapirs are declining in numbers be-cause of man, partly through hunting and partly through man's destruction of the forest. A tapir's snout is its most distinguishing feature, a short, flexible proboscis that looks like an abbreviated elephant trunk. With it the tapir can pull leaves and grass into its mouth or lie submerged, with only its nostrils above the water's surface.

The Almost-pig

THE PECCARIES OF THE NEW WORLD are so much like pigs in appearance that in common speech they are often *called* pigs. Actually, while they are very closely related to the true pigs of the Old World, they differ from them internally in a number of ways, and are accordingly placed in a family of their own. The collared peccary or javelina of Mexico and south-western United States is a trim creature, covered with a close coat of stiff, grizzled hair. When alarmed the peccary bristles on the back and neck, and exposes a powerful musk gland located over its hips. The scent from this gland is very strong, and can carry far.

The peccary lives and moves about in groups of a dozen or more; normally the animals are inoffensive, but when danger threatens they become aggressive, and will put even a bobcat to flight. Like most desert animals, peccaries spend the major part of the day resting in whatever shade they can find, moving about at night and in the early morning in search of roots, berries and other vegetation. Like the true pigs, the peccary does not disdain flesh, and sometimes eats small vertebrates.

Neither Deer nor Mouse

THE DENSE FORESTS of the world's tropics are a perfect habitat for small, herbivorous animals. In the New World this niche has been filled by agoutis, rabbit-sized rodents with thin, delicate limbs. In the tropics of the Old World rodents never developed to fit the niche, which

(above)
Looking like a tiny deer, the **water chevrotain,** actually a relative of camels and pigs, is one of the smallest hoofed mammals in the world. Its small size makes it vulnerable to many predators, so it stays in dense vegetation along rivers and often escapes danger by diving into the water.

(left)
Excessively timid and nervous creatures, the **agoutis** of South America can make tremendous leaps when frightened by outsiders, but they are often extremely violent to one another.

became filled instead by chevrotains, hoofed animals no bigger than the agoutis. One species, the small Malayan chevrotain, stands scarcely twelve inches high at the shoulder. It looks something like a tiny deer, but is more nearly related to camels and pigs despite its appearance. Male chevrotains have enlarged tusks whose function is unknown.

Although the female has but a single fawn at a time, she is capable of breeding again immediately after giving birth, and by the time her fawn has reached its full growth, at the age of five months, she can give birth to another fawn. The mother chevrotain leaves her baby in a sheltered place, a crevice in the rocks or a hollow stump, and returns to it several times a day to nurse it. With females capable of producing a fawn every five months overpopulation might seem inevitable, but this does not happen, probably because the chevrotains' small size makes them susceptible to attack by even the smaller carnivores.

The Deer That Barks

O NE OF THE SMALLER of the world's deer, the muntjac stands less than two feet tall at the shoulder. A native of Asia, the muntjac prefers thickly grown areas, where its small size gives it a slight advantage over the larger predators. Males carry a pair of small, simple antlers, with just a hint of a fork, but they are peculiar in that the pedicels, the bony, haired projections from the skull on which the antlers grow, are elongated and may be nearly as long as the antlers themselves. The male has enlarged tusks in the upper jaw as well. Females have smaller tusks and lack antlers, although they do have short pedicels, each with a tuft of hair. During the mating season muntjacs utter a sharp, barking call, and they have a similar bark which they sound when danger threatens. Six months after mating the female gives birth to her fawn (occasionally to twins), which she leaves in a secluded place, returning at intervals to nurse it until it is old enough to follow her around.

(bottom left)
The odd pattern of markings of the **okapi** makes it less conspicuous in the dappled light of the deep Congo forests.

(bottom right)
During the mating season or when danger threatens, the **muntjac,** a small Asian deer, utters a sharp, barking call that has earned it the name "barking deer."

Usually found grazing in large herds in grassy regions and sparse woodlands, the beautiful, spotted **axis deer** of India and Ceylon is a good swimmer and readily takes to water.

Like Son, Like Father

THE AXIS DEER, or chital, is one of the handsomest of the deer family. Its fawns, like those of most deer, are spotted at birth, but while almost all kinds of spotted fawns lose their markings as they grow and take on a uniform coat of brown, the axis deer keeps its rich, golden-brown coat and white spots throughout its life. Axis deer are gregarious. In parts of India and Ceylon herds of nearly a hundred animals can be found in open grassy areas and sparse forest. Often a number of males live with the herd, for they seem to be less aggressive than most deer.

The "Zebra" That Was a "Giraffe"

IN THE BEGINNING of this century, when Europeans were only beginning to penetrate the equatorial forests of Africa, an explorer found in a pigmy village a strip of tanned hide that bore a series of blackish and white stripes. He was most interested in this find, for zebras are animals of the grasslands, not of the forest, and a forest-dwelling zebra would be an important scientific discovery. When at last the pigmies showed him the animal from which the leather came it turned out to be not a zebra but the animal we know today as the okapi, an odd, forest-living relative of the giraffe.

The okapi is a rich chestnut hue, except for its legs and rump, which bear alternating light and dark horizontal stripes. The okapi's neck is quite short, for a long neck is not suited to an animal which must be able to travel rapidly through the thick forest growth; its tongue, however, is like the giraffe's, long and prehensile, enabling its owner to pull

(top left)
Exterminated everywhere but in Corsica and Sardinia, the **mouflon** has been hunted by man for centuries, and only a few herds are left. Stricter protective laws are now ensuring its survival.

(top right)
The long, twisted horns of the **markhor,** a magnificent wild goat of the mountains of India and other parts of Asia, measure as much as three feet and, depending on the race of markhor, can be tightly or loosely twisted.

down leaves that would otherwise be out of reach. Okapis appear to be numerous in their native haunt, the Ituri Forest of the Congo, but so wary are they that few people, even the pigmies, have ever seen a wild one. Since they cannot hunt the okapi in a normal fashion, the pigmies capture them in concealed pits, which they dig along the okapis' trails.

As Different as Black and White

MANY KINDS OF MAMMALS, such as the spotted fawn of a whitetail deer or the rusty-red calf of the bison, look very different from their parents at birth, but quickly grow to resemble them. The baby blesbok, however, instead of growing more like its parents every day seems for a long time to be trying to look less like them. The adult blesboks are rich, reddish-brown antelopes with a white marking, or blaze, on the snout and forehead. The baby, however, is a pale sandy tone, well suited to make it inconspicuous in the dried grass of its home in southern Africa. It has no markings on the face to speak of. Then, as it grows, the fawn begins to develop its parents' facial markings—but in a rich black, not white. Not until its second year does this strange condition begin to change, as white hairs gradually appear among the black, slowly replacing them. Herds of long-faced blesboks graze peacefully on the plains, as several of the older animals stand alertly on a rise or the low mound of an anthill, watching for danger.

Haven in the Heather

OF ALL THE WILD SHEEP of the world the little mouflon is probably the most attractive, with its chestnut, white and black coat. Once found on many islands in the Mediterranean Sea, it has been exterminated everywhere except on the islands of Corsica and Sardinia. High in the mountains on these two islands there grows a kind of heather, often as tall as a man, into which the mouflon can disappear upon the approach of danger. The heather provides the mouflon with shelter from bad weather, too, and has been credited with the survival of the sheep. Early in the morning and at twilight the mouflon leaves the heather to graze in open grassy areas. Still, men have hunted the mouflon for centuries, and only strict protection by law will ensure its continued existence.

Patriarch of the Mountains

THE MARKHOR, a magnificent wild goat native to the mountains of Southern Asia, is a magnificent beast. As it stands on a rocky promontory, the male, with its black beard and long spiralling horns, is a sight no one can view without awe. Four races of markhor exist, distinguished by the shape of their horns. The Kabul markhor wears its horns in two straight corkscrews that diverge toward the tips to form a V shape. At the other extreme the Astor markhor's horns grow in an open spiral and diverge widely. The markhor lives under a variety of climatic conditions, some of them in places that know extreme cold in winter and sweltering heat in summer. In general, however, this handsome goat moves to lower elevations with the approach of winter, returning to the high crags in summer.

Something Like a Cow

FROM THE MISHMI HILLS of northern Burma eastward into China lives a heavy-bodied relative of the arctic muskox. The takin looks something like a mixture of cow, muskox and mountain goat, and has a

(above)
While herds of long-faced **blesboks** graze on the grassy plains of South Africa, older members of the herds stand guard on a rise or low anthill mound to watch for danger.

(left)
Ranging the mountain valleys of Central Asia, the **takin** is a cousin of the musk ox of the Arctic, but its unique appearance confused zoologists for a long time. The coat of one race is a beautiful metallic gold color.

The strange black-and-white markings of the **Malay tapir** make it less noticeable to tigers and leopards as it browses in deep forests at night.

strong musky scent that is noticeable at a distance. It makes its home high in the hills where there are few humans. Although clumsy in appearance, the takin is a skillful climber, with broad stout hoofs to give it purchase. During the heat of the day takins generally rest in rhododendron or other thickets; they are active primarily at dusk, except during cool weather, when they may move about all day.

Only three takins have ever been seen outside their native land, two in the London Zoo many years ago and one in the Bronx Zoo. The last animal, a female named Gracie, arrived in 1959, and was so discomforted by the heat of summer that she had to be given an air-conditioned stall in which to rest on hot days. She became almost as tame as a domesticated cow, and grew inordinately fond of bananas, a food she would never have encountered in her native hill country.

NATURE HOBBIES

As an activity, a hobby may be lightly taken up, erratically attended to and easily dropped, it may be a serious, intense, lifetime interest, or its pursuit may fall somewhere between these extremes. In any event, hobbies are generally thought of as peripheral, even extraneous, to our main concerns, regardless of the ardor and enthusiasm of the hobbyist or the meticulousness with which he tends to his avocation. Perhaps this is a wrong idea.

Certainly hobbies are part of our exploration of the world around us and, in a wider sense, of our search for knowledge. They enrich our experience, broaden our horizons and give us new insights into all aspects of our lives. This is especially true in the case of nature hobbies, each of which is a doorway to the world of nature, for none of our occupations can ever be wholly divorced from other living things or from the materials that make up our planet. Bringing us into closer contact with these, nature hobbies familiarize us with many plants, animals and substances that may not lie close to hand and, in so doing, make them part of our daily surroundings.

The keeping of tropical fish is one of the most popular hobbies today, and AQUARIUM FISHES introduces us to some of the colorful and exotic inhabitants of miniature, glass-enclosed, underwater worlds. Unobtrusive and requiring little care, aquarium fishes reward their keepers with endless delightful and intriguing spectacles.

Growing plants indoors enables us to live, at least to some extent, among the beauty of leaves and flowers. HOUSE PLANTS acquaints us with the enormous variety of decorative plants, each of which—as every gardener knows—has its own personality and way of responding to the grower.

Differing in age, materials and origin, and sometimes containing valuable ores and beautiful gems, rocks are the natural deposits making up much of the earth's crust. While showing us, then, some of the most dazzling and colorful stones, ROCKS, MINERALS AND GEMS also considers the plainer, but no less important, "building blocks" of our planet.

SHELLS investigates the hard outer coverings of soft-bodied mollusks such as clams, scallops and snails. Found in some of the most varied environments in the world and coveted for their rarity, their delicate patterns and the fineness of their designs, shells have been collected for thousands of years and have even been used as money.

► *A whole miniature water world within four transparent walls for delightful observation.*

Aquarium Fishes

WHEN ANYONE TAKES UP a new and exciting hobby, he at once seizes every opportunity to convert all his friends; he wants to share his fascinating new fun with them, and to enjoy seeing their enthusiasm for his own wonderful discovery. And when this new hobby can give men, women and whole families such thrills as fish-keeping does, the hobby is likely to spread through the community before very long.

That is why many millions of homes now proudly exhibit carefully tended and beautifully displayed aquaria. In them billions of tiny fish of many hues are admired, added to, exchanged among friends, enthusiastically bred, sold and enjoyed by both children and adults.

If you are a dinner guest in a home where the fish hobby has fascinated the family, you will be quickly invited to admire the latest additions to the aquarium. Whatever you say about it, don't make the mistake of thinking that the tank you are asked to appreciate is no more than a glorified goldfish bowl! The modern aquarium—with its thermostatically controlled heater and its fluorescent-lighted dome cover—is in step with today's streamlined and gadget-operated car, a possession that calls for admiration, and gets it from all comers!

You'll Be a Fan Before You Know It

HERE'S A HOBBY FOR THE WHOLE FAMILY. It gives every member the interest and pleasure of having pets, without the drawbacks that often come with the need to walk, feed, bathe and comb them. Fishes are neither noisy nor dirty. They don't trail mud in on the living-room rug, nor scatter birdseed over the sofa, and no unpleasant smells are ever associated with them.

When properly established, your aquarium can safely be left to itself

Beneath the surface of tropical seas and rivers live some of nature's most spectacular creatures. Many of these fishes are brilliantly colored, while others have strange and unusual shapes. All of them are delightful to watch. With a minimal amount of attention, tropical fish will live happily for years inside the home aquarium. However, not all of them live equally well together. For instance, the beautiful **zebra cichlid** (insert, top right) will fight not only other fish but also its own kind. It attacks swiftly and without warning. Its poor behavior, not typical of most tropical fish, makes it difficult to keep in any but the largest aquariums.

MEL HUNTER

while you are away for a couple of weeks in the summer. And when you are home, it can offer you such a variety of interesting entertainment that you are repaid a hundredfold for the minimum of attention it calls for.

Here, within four transparent walls, is a whole miniature water world for your pleasure and instruction. It offers never-ending and beautiful activity for study and delightful observation—for people of all ages. It can show you and your children the strange and striking shapes, habits and hues of a great variety of tiny fish.

You will have a ringside seat for courtings, marriages, births, baby-sittings, robberies, murders, processions and picnics. They take place in the bright crystal tank before your surprised and fascinated gaze.

A Litter of Kittens or Puppies Was Never Like This

THE PLEASURE THAT COMES FROM KEEPING PETS can be enormously increased by breeding them. Here is where fish give an overflowing measure of interest, enjoyment and instruction—with the least possible trouble on your part.

In a suitable and controlled aquarium, your pets will multiply rapidly; their astonishingly varied breeding habits will be a constantly interesting spectacle. Some species build nests, vigilantly guard and fan the eggs, tirelessly tend and exercise the babies.

At least one species scoops out a nest in the sand for its young. When they are big enough to swim, you will see the entire family parade around the tank. This happens only in the daytime; at night the young fish are kept "in bed" under the parents' watchful eyes.

The guppies, swordtails and several other varieties bring forth their young alive; they swim off as soon as they are dropped! This habit makes possible one of the high spots of fascination in keeping your aquarium. By providing a small breeding cage—hooked on to the side of the tank—you can isolate a live-bearing female when she is ready to give birth to her offspring.

The "mouth-breeding" tropicals carry and hatch their eggs in their mouths; they take no food during the days the fry are hatching out; and for several days after, the little ones shoot back into the friendly mouth-cavern when alarmed.

How This Fascinating Hobby Started

THE WELL-KNOWN TERM "TROPICAL FISH", and the fact that most aquaria must be artificially heated in winter, are sufficient indication that the first of these lovely little jewel-like creatures were imported from tropical climes. The craze for having them in home aquaria started in Germany and has now spread to all other parts of the world.

As the hobby developed a really important market for pet shop dealers, the whole equatorial region of the world was searched for new

Certainly one of the most spectacular of all fish, the **lionfish** has poison glands at the base of each dorsal spine. The sting of a large fish may be as dangerous as a poisonous snake bite.

and beautiful miniature varieties. Swamps, ditches, rain pools, flooded rice-fields, mountain streams, lakes and rivers in Egypt, Australia, India, China, Thailand, Florida, Panama and South America have been dipped and seined by hundreds of amateur and professional fish hunters.

What Makes a Fish "Tropical"?

IT IS OBVIOUS THAT TROPICAL FISHES are those that thrive in a tropical environment. The ideal water temperature for them is 75° F. In summer the average daily temperature, with its normal fluctuations, usually suits tropical fishes well. But winter involves the problem of maintaining the aquarium at 75° by the use of a heater, controlled by a suitable thermostat. This type of heater is constructed to keep the water of the aquarium at a pre-set temperature.

The words "tropical fishes", as they apply to your aquarium, ordinarily refer to *freshwater* fishes. Ordinary tap water is excellent, provided that it is left exposed to the air long enough for the escape of gases that may have been used as disinfecting agents. Pet shops have special pills to make water suitable for fishes.

The tap water should be added to the aquarium slowly, on top of clean aquarium gravel. Use two pounds of ⚹2 or ⚹3 gravel, well washed, for every gallon of water your aquarium holds. Though the average amateur seldom even attempts to keep a salt-water aquarium, the marine set-up is just as rewarding and fascinating as a freshwater tank. Many very different fishes are available, collected mostly from tropical reefs around the world. In addition, anyone living near the seacoast can collect his own specimens with very little effort, and thus participate in his hobby to a much greater extent.

Sea water just as it comes from the sea is not suitable for a marine aquarium, but prepared salt can be mixed with pure water to make a good solution. It is desirable to add some natural sea water, usually between ten and fifty per cent. Sometimes sea water is evaporated to brine, then diluted with fresh water. In any case, salinity should be about 1.025, and acidity pH 8.2.

Aquarium keeping is not an expensive hobby; you will find that a five-gallon tank can be completely equipped for no more than would be spent on quite a modest price camera, and this includes the heater, fishes, plants, gravel and other essentials.

What Is a Balanced Aquarium?

IN THE FOLLOWING PAGES we will give you detailed advice about the kinds of fish that will thrive best together in your aquarium, but first we must deal with a piece of misinformation that is quite generally believed to be a fact.

Many books about fish-keeping use the term, a *balanced aquarium*. The theory of the so-called balanced aquarium suggests that aquatic

Headstanders continually swim and feed in a "standing on head" position. They help keep a tank clean by grubbing bits of food from the bottom.

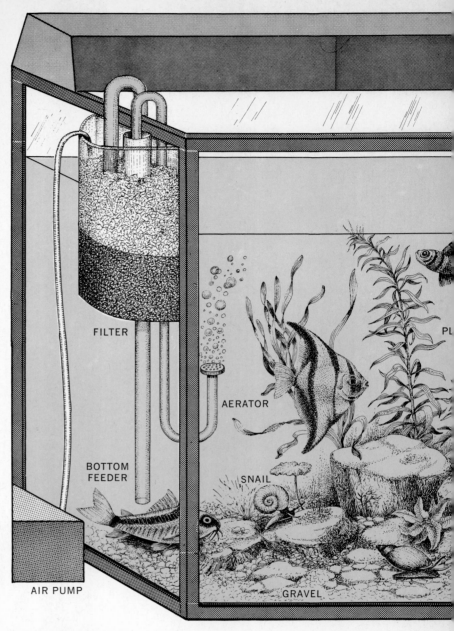

FILTER

AERATOR

PL

BOTTOM
FEEDER

SNAIL

AIR PUMP

GRAVEL

Well-balanced aquariums have important devices for measuring and controlling the oxygen content and temperature and for filtering the water. Proper lighting, which makes aquariums more attractive for viewing, also serves to stimulate the growth of aquatic plants.

plants in an aquarium give oxygen to the water in exchange for the carbon dioxide gas dissolved in it—which the plants use in their growth processes.

And then, since the fishes need oxygen to live, and give off carbon dioxide as waste, they are supposed to exchange it for the oxygen the plants furnish, with benefit to both parties. Most books on aquarium management accordingly urge the use of ample plants, in order to supply the "balance" of oxygen needed by an ample number of fish.

This theory of the balanced aquarium has been scientifically proven

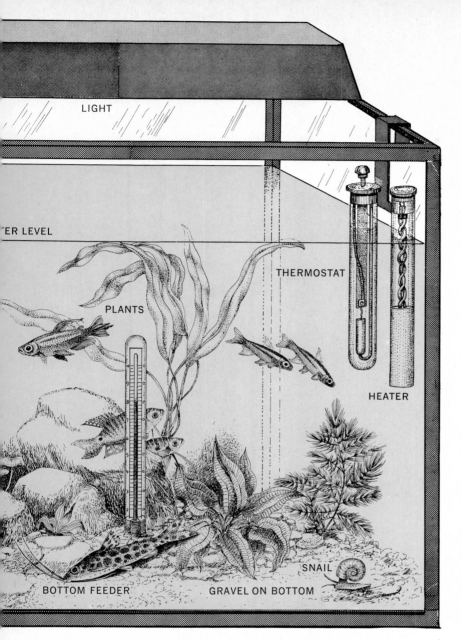

LIGHT

WATER LEVEL

THERMOSTAT

PLANTS

HEATER

SNAIL

BOTTOM FEEDER   GRAVEL ON BOTTOM

Scavengers such as snails and bottom-feeding fish help keep the aquarium clean by eating bits of food that the other occupants of the tank have either missed or rejected. In addition, snails keep down the growth of algae that form on the glass and plants.

to be a false one. We had better give you the truth about it in the beginning: the little oxygen that the aquarium plants give off to the water could not possibly supply the needs of the fishes; most of the oxygen dissolved in the water—the oxygen the fish breathe—is absorbed from the surrounding atmosphere.

The term *balanced aquarium*, then, is thoroughly misleading and should be discarded. The proper number of fish to put in a gallon of water will be covered in the following directions, which enable your fish to stay vigorously alive.

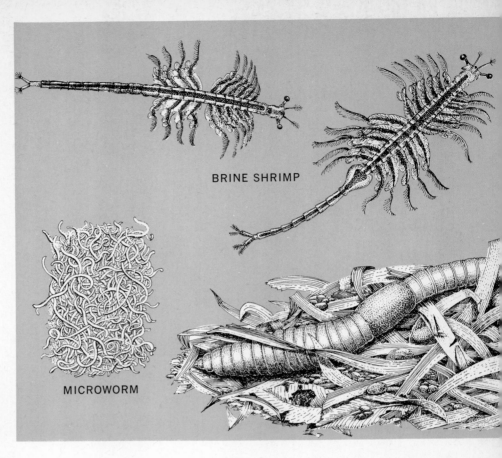

BRINE SHRIMP

MICROWORM

Many living creatures may be used as food in an aquarium. The common earthworm, when cut into small pieces, will be eaten by almost any fish, even by one that is normally a vegetarian.

What Are the Four Classes of Aquarium Fishes?

FISHES, LIKE OTHER ANIMALS, have definite temperaments. You will need to know the habits of the various species in order to start a successful community aquarium. By *community* aquarium we mean one in which more than one species of fish is maintained.

Aquarium fishes are generally placed in four large classes. These are, at times, arbitrary: a single species of fish might occur in more than one class, depending upon its nature and habits. These classes are: *the egg layers,* those fishes which reproduce by laying eggs; *the livebearers,* those which reproduce by bearing their young alive; *the bubble nest builders,* those that build a nest in which to deposit their spawn; and finally, *the scavengers,* those which eat what the other fishes leave behind. Actually, the bubble nest builder could also be an egg layer—and more than one scavenger builds a bubble nest. For our purposes, a scavenger will be any fish such as the clown loach from Borneo with a mouth which opens underneath. The peculiar mouth parts of a scavenger are specially adapted for poking about the gravel, picking up bits of food which the top-feeding fishes (fishes whose

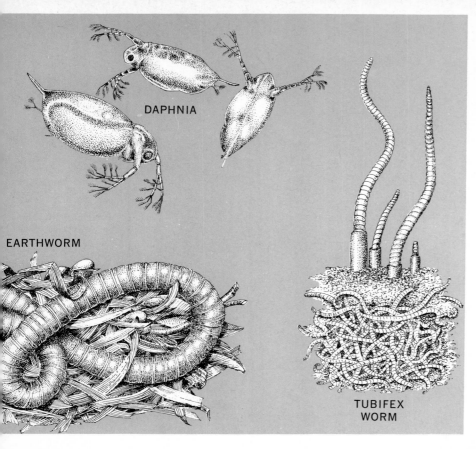

DAPHNIA

EARTHWORM

TUBIFEX
WORM

mouths open like a scoop from the top), such as the zebrafish or the hatchetfish, fail to eat before it falls to the bottom of the aquarium and which the middle swimmers fail to catch on the way down. The middle swimmers, such as the beautiful angelfish, have mouth parts which open up in a line parallel with their bodies.

Two Simple Rules for a Successful Aquarium

IN MAKING A SELECTION OF FISH for the home aquarium, avoid purchasing predators. Select an equal number of top feeders, middle swimmers and scavengers. Never get more than two fish for every gallon of aquarium water unless the fish are less than one inch long. A safe rule to follow—so you won't overcrowd the aquarium—is: *Do not put more than two inches of fish in each gallon of water.*

Though these fishes do not overeat, they can become ill from eating food which has become foul by lying about in the aquarium. Overfeeding ruins more aquaria than *all* other causes put together. Feed mature fishes once a day; don't give them more than they will eat eagerly in two minutes. Baby fishes may be fed twice a day, but again,

In nature the brightly colored **clownfish** always stays close to the poisonous sea anemone, ready to take refuge among the deadly tentacles. Why this fish remains unharmed by the poisons has baffled scientists.

do not feed them more than they can eat in two minutes. Cloudy aquarium water results directly from overfeeding. If your aquarium becomes cloudy, stop feeding your fish until it clears up. The aquarium should never need a change of water if the fishes are not overfed. If you follow these simple rules, you should be successful with your aquarium.

The Angelfish—a Model Parent

THE ANGELFISH IS ONE OF THE MOST POPULAR, distinguished and beautiful of all aquarium fishes. Its scientific name is *Pterophyllum scalare*. This fish originates in the Amazon River in South America and has long been one of the most popular of aquarium fishes. It is a graceful swimmer with its shimmering fins, sparkling scales and interesting shape. The angelfish belongs to a group of fishes known scientifically as the *cichlids*.

Cichlids as a class show extreme parental care; the angelfish is no exception. It breeds readily in the home aquarium once it is about one year old. The parents will hustle about looking for a clean, firm, flat surface upon which to place their spawn. Once they find a flat rock (a piece of slate, slanted against the side of the aquarium, usually satisfies the breeders) or a broad firm leaf, they will scrub the area spotlessly clean with their jaws. Then the female will advance upon the spot and deposit one long row of pearly eggs, each about the size of a large pinhead. Immediately after the female has finished one row of eggs, the male will chase her away with a short, abrupt peck, and run over the same course, fertilizing the eggs. This process will be repeated for hours, with the female laying parallel rows of eggs on the slate or leaf. If the pair is left alone and not disturbed, they will take turns guarding and "fanning" the eggs. This fanning process, accomplished by the rapid movement of the fish's fins, sends steady streams of water over the eggs, and serves to keep debris from settling on them. It also insures the eggs a constant supply of oxygenated water. You must remember that developing eggs, like living fishes, require oxygen.

(bottom left)
During mating the red-orange belly of the **firemouth cichlid** becomes particularly brilliant, especially in the female. This fish, which has been successfully bred many times, is a good parent to its offspring.

(bottom right)
Like other cichlids, of which it is a variety, the graceful **angelfish** makes an excellent parent. It breeds readily in home aquariums. Sometimes this fish suffers an inexplicable loss of appetite; however, it seldom actually starves.

But the Babies Must Be Kept "On Leash"

Aﬀᴛᴇʀ ᴛʜʀᴇᴇ ᴅᴀʏꜱ ᴛʜᴇ ꜰʀʏ are all hatched from their eggs, but they remain attached by a single strong filament to the spot upon which they were laid, and are held fast against the current caused by the incessant fanning of the parents. A week after being spawned, the young will be free-swimming, and look like any "ordinary" fish. It will be three weeks before they begin to take on the characteristic appearance of their parents. In commercial fish hatcheries the eggs are removed from the parents and reared artificially. The fanning process is successfully imitated either by running water or by air forced over the eggs under the water.

If the parent fish are frightened or otherwise put out while fanning, they will devour their own spawn. Most fishes, in fact, are cannibalistic toward their fry, and various attempts have been made to explain "why" the spawn will be devoured on one occasion and so painstakingly nurtured the next; but no satisfactory explanation has been offered.

The cichlids, taken as a whole, seem to be pugnacious fighters, by their very nature. Hobbyists with large tanks may have tried keeping the larger species which grow to eight inches in length. They then find out two things; that many cichlids have a habit of digging in the sand or gravel and uprooting whatever plants they can find, and that a fish this size can make a shambles of the best-planned aquarium! For all that, they are interesting fish, and some species are very handsome. The Jack Dempsey, named for its size and pugnacity, is a lovely deep blackish-brown and covered with brilliant spots which range from gold to bright blue on a single individual. The eye is a clear, pure red, and there is a red edge to the dorsal fin.

(above)
A most unusual and exotic fish, the **leaf fish** looks and acts remarkably like a floating leaf. It lives on smaller fishes and has a voracious appetite, making it difficult to keep in the average aquarium.

You Will Probably Prefer Dwarf Cichlids

Tʜᴏᴜɢʜ ꜱᴏᴍᴇ ᴄɪᴄʜʟɪᴅꜱ are very large, others are very small. In the aquarium we are always more interested in the smaller fishes. Two very closely related dwarf cichlids are the African dwarfs, *Pelmatochromis kribensis* and the *Pelmatochromis teniatus*. These small beauties from Africa are very shy about their spawning habits. A popular spawning site is the inside of an overturned flowerpot in which a small hole has been bored as an entrance. The dwarf cichlids usually take good care of their young, though we sometimes hear reports of "infanticide".

There is only one large cichlid found in North America: it is a close relative of the family of sunfishes. Ordinarily, fish scientists consider the sunfishes as cold-water fishes, not tropical fishes at all; but the fiery beauty of the black-banded sunfish, *Mesagonistius chaetodon*, a native of the lake waters from southern New Jersey to South Carolina, has

(below)
Before the introduction of angelfish, the **Jack Dempsey** was quite popular with aquarium enthusiasts. Often living for ten years or longer, its vibrant colors deepen with age.

encouraged its adoption in American aquaria. The fish itself is not too peaceful and ought not to be kept with fishes smaller than itself. This rule of size is very important, and it is usually safe to keep fishes of the same size in the same aquarium. At least then you are sure that the fish will not eat each other in one big gulp!

The black-banded sunfish breed easily, exactly like the cichlids. They take good care of their young; build a fine, clean nest in which to spawn; and make interesting aquarium inhabitants once they have properly "settled in". This is a good fish for the beginner as it does not require a heated aquarium.

All the Cichlids Are Egg Layers

THERE ARE SOME INTERESTING CICHLIDS which hatch their spawn in their mouths. These fishes, usually called "mouth breeders", keep the eggs and fry in their mouths until the babies are large enough to fend for themselves. This means that, for several weeks at least, the fish must go without food, since it could hardly eat with a mouthful of its own young. The great individual care given to its spawn by the large black-banded sunfish is closely matched by the Siamese fighting fish.

Fine Aquarium Fish—Siamese Fighters

IN THAILAND THERE ABOUNDS a small bright-hued fish known to scientists as *Betta splendens*. This fish breathes atmospheric air in addition to taking some oxygen from the water. It could not survive long if it did not occasionally push its snout above the water surface for a gulp of fresh air. This has been scientifically established. The popular name "fighting fish" is derived from the Siamese popular name for this fish. In Thailand the fish are bred for their fighting ability and stamina. If two male fish are placed together in the same aquarium they will fight continually, tearing their fins to shreds, until one of the two fish gives up and refuses to attack or retaliate. He then merely runs from his antagonist. Stories that the fish fight to the death are ridiculous. The fish heal quickly and are always eager and willing to start a battle. Wagers are placed upon these fighting fish in public contests in Thailand.

The fighting ability, and pigmentation of the fighting fish are alone enough to account for the millions of fighters bred annually in the United States. But their breeding habits, and the interesting varieties of different hues which have been developed through the years, play an important part in their popularity.

The blood-red fighting fish is a new red variety, developed in Europe recently. The males have the usual long flowing fins and the females have similar but shorter fins. The cornflower-blue fighting fish has been established for a long time and much improvement has been made

In Thailand the **Siamese fighting fish** is bred for its fighting ability. Contrary to popular belief, this fish does not fight to the death. The loser of a battle merely runs away from his opponent, thus ending the contest.

(left)
Sucker catfish will eat anything but are particularly useful for eliminating algae from plants and aquarium glass. Because they are bullies and will eat other scavenger fish, one to a tank is best.

(below)
Like Siamese fighting fishes, two male **halfbeaks** will fight until one is well established as the dominant member of a group. Young halfbeaks do not hatch from deposited eggs but are born alive.

in its finnage through selective breeding. One variety, the orchid Cambodia fighting fish, was developed from the Cambodia fighting fish (a flesh-toned variety) and the red and blue varieties. This species is becoming increasingly popular. All breeders are attempting to develop a pure black fighting fish, and although none has been successful to date some dark purple fish do appear from time to time.

And What a Fiery Lover Is the Fighting Fish!

WHEN A MALE AND FEMALE FIGHTING FISH are placed together in the same aquarium and both are ready for breeding, which is nearly always, they show immediate interest in each other. The male, in his clumsy attempts at romance, often tears a few bits off the female's fins, but after a relatively short time he will begin to prepare his bubble nest. This is composed of muscus-covered bubbles which he produces by gulping mouthfuls of air at the surface of the water; these he releases in a stream and they form a mass. The bubbles stick together and eventually a huge nest, some three inches in diameter and fully an inch thick, will slowly develop. When it is complete the male again drives the female . . . this time with greater finesse. Over and over again he will rapidly approach her . . . stop short of his goal—and hastily beat a retreat under his nest. He is inviting the female to join him. Many times he dances beautifully, with fins fully extended in magnificent display, in order to entice her to his lair. Finally she succumbs to his charms and joins him beneath the nest of bubbles.

With the expulsion of the eggs, the female is paralyzed for a few seconds, while the male catches the slowly falling eggs in his mouth before they reach the bottom of the aquarium. No sooner does he catch the last egg than the female "wakes up" and the male deposits the fertilized eggs safely in his bubble nest. Oftentimes the female isn't

(right, color insert)
Midget races of larger fishes are well suited to a home aquarium. The **harlequin serranid** is a very small sea bass. Its markings are effective camouflage in its natural habitat.

"knocked out" long enough and she "helps" the male with his task . . . but instead of spitting the eggs into the bubble nest, she usually swallows them! Once spawning is completed she again becomes reluctant to join him under the nest, and should then be removed. The male should be left alone with his children to guard them and to blow more bubbles; these keep his progeny at the surface of the water, near to the oxygen supply they need so much. After a few days the eggs hatch and the male must try to keep the wriggling mass of youngsters

(left)
Different species of fish vary widely as to where and how they deposit their eggs. They may be left on vegetation above or below the surface, inserted into shellfish, held in the mouth, buried, or laid in various sorts of "nests."

① Egg Implanting in Mussels
② Mouth Breeder
③ Egg Burier
④ Bubble Nest Builder
⑤ Nest Builder
⑥ Sand Nest
⑦ Eggs Glued to Grass
⑧ Eggs Laid on Grass Mat on Gravel
⑨ Top Spawners
⓪ Egg Splashing

together. Finally he gives up and either ignores the babies—or, more usually, begins to eat them. He should be removed as soon as the fry are free swimming—if you want to raise several hundred fighting fish.

Fine Specimens Aren't Allowed to Fight

IN COMMERCIAL HATCHERIES IN FLORIDA tens of thousands of quart jars are used to keep the male fish separate during their entire lifetime. This is necessary to ensure that their finnage develops perfectly and unscarred; when perfect, they command a handsome price in the pet shops. The usual price for a male fighting fish is about $3.00, though there are exceptionally gorgeous ones that are much higher, and poorer specimens that are much cheaper. Baby fighting fish, however, are sold very reasonably.

Special Siamese fighting fish display tanks are made with glass partitions which allow the fish to see each other, but which prevent them from making physical contact.

The Fish That Glows Like a Neon Sign

ANOTHER VERY POPULAR AND BEAUTIFUL aquarium fish is the neon tetra, *Hyphessobrycon innesi*. The scientific species name of this fish is *innesi*. It was named after William T. Innes, "dean of American aquarists". Innes, recently given an honorary doctorate for his great work in advancing the aquarium hobby, has been an active and ardent fish fancier for many years.

The popular name, neon tetra, was given to the fish by the same people who gave it the scientific name, and one look at a healthy specimen is enough to show you why. This fish grows very slowly, reaching its maximum size of less than two inches in about three years. The older it becomes, the more electrifying is its hue. A tankful of these beauties has never failed to cause a chorus of "Oh's" and "Ah's", and the fish is considered one of the best fish for the community aquarium. It is as peaceful as it is beautiful, but its breeding presents a difficult challenge. The persistent aquarist, however, seldom gives up until he is successful, and tank-bred neons are now rather common.

This fish, once seen, is never forgotten, and the aquarium world owes a great debt of thanks to Mr. Auguste Rabaut, the American fish and orchid-collector who discovered these fish in an inland Brazilian river. Only through great sacrifice and effort was he able to transport the fish 2,000 miles to the coast so they could be flown to aquarists all over the world.

Known the world over for its brilliant coloring, the **neon tetra** is easy to keep but nearly impossible to breed. Its pleasant disposition makes it a welcome addition to any aquarium.

Unlike the neon tetra, which it resembles, the **cardinal tetra** breeds readily, and the young grow very rapidly. Many enthusiasts consider it the most beautiful fish ever to have appeared on the aquarium scene. It is a rather recent addition, first collected from Brazil in 1952.

Also in South America we find other small, extremely beautiful fishes of this same genus *Hyphessobrycon,* commonly called "tetras". The Serpae tetra, *Hyphessobrycon callistus,* found near Serpa, has been known by incorrect names to aquarists. This was due to the various tonal varieties in which the fish appears. Sometimes slight differences in hue are mistaken for a different species by young, overeager scientists. It remains for the aquarist to stimulate the fish scientists to produce enough specimens to prove beyond a doubt that many varieties *are* mere varieties and not distinct species.

The Ubiquitous Guppy

To THE AVERAGE MAN-ON-THE-STREET, especially in previous years, a home aquarium has often meant no more than a "tankful of guppies", and, although every aquarist knows this to be a very false idea, the guppy has long enjoyed widespread popularity and attention. This species, originally from Trinidad, Barbados, the Guianas and Venezuela, has been intensively bred and crossbred for so long that there are few if any of the original characteristics left! Hardly a year goes by without the breeding of a new (and sometimes expensive) super-guppy. Lately the trend has been toward developing a long, flowing tail, and some of the results have been amazing; we have seen males with tails almost as long as their bodies, some of them fanning out and displaying dazzling hues. Others have elongated rays in the upper or lower edge of the tail. These are known as "top-swords" and "bottom-swords". Those with rays both above and below are called "lyre-tails", and those with long central rays "pin-tails". Others have been bred for hue—gold, blue, green, red, "lace-tail", "English", "Trini-

Perhaps the most popular fishes among beginners are **guppies.** These hospitable little creatures almost raise themselves. They breed readily, grow rapidly, take any kind of food, and can even stand foul water.

dad" and so forth. Females are almost uniformly grey, though the gold species has a yellow female. Guppies will eat a varied diet, and require nothing more than a clean, uncrowded aquarium kept at about 75°. Youngsters should be fed newly-hatched brine shrimp for a week or two to assure their full size, good health and bright tones as adults.

As we have mentioned, a home aquarium will benefit from the presence of some sort of scavenging fish. Some species commonly used are sucker catfish, armoured catfish, weatherfish and some gobies. Tadpoles and freshwater or salt-water shrimp are also used, as are snails of various kinds.

The subject of snails is bound to stir up a controversy whenever aquarists get together. Some consider them a blessing; others loudly proclaim them a nuisance. Certainly there is no place for them in a breeding aquarium when eggs are present. There are few things as tasty to a hungry snail as a freshly laid batch of fish eggs, and what they do not eat they will as likely as not break. On the other hand, snails can and do perform useful functions in an aquarium where young fishes are being raised. It is sometimes difficult for the aquarist to judge exactly how much to feed his growing fishes. Underfeeding is likely to stunt their growth; but the water will quickly foul if he overfeeds, and most of his youngsters will be found lying on the bottom in a very short time. If there are snails present, cleaning up the surplus food, the dangers attendant on overfeeding are lessened.

But it must be said that snails do little that cannot be accomplished by a good water-circulation and filtration system in a well-balanced aquarium—although one cannot deny that they convert leftover food into droppings which are easily broken down and then absorbed by the plants or removed by the filter. Snails are also used as food for the larger fishes, and one species was formerly used as a producer of *infusoria*—a culture rich in microscopic animals, widely used as food for tiny newly hatched fishes.

Lovely Pencilfishes and Odd Hatchetfishes

MOST OF THE AQUARIUM FISHES popular in the United States come from South America. Oddities among them include the attractive pencilfishes, typified by the dwarf pencilfish, *Mannostomus marginatus.* The pencilfishes get their name from their slender pencil-like shape. All are long, thin fishes with beautiful red, yellow and brown markings. Along with the pencilfishes, usually in the same waters, there occurs one of the oddest of all aquarium fishes . . . the hatchetfishes. This group of fishes is known for the deeply compressed body and the hatchet-shaped appearance of the sharply curved ventral surface. The silver hatchetfish, *Gasteropelecus levis,* beautifully illustrates the physical characteristics which enable this fish to "fly".

It is one of the famous South American flying fishes, and reports have it that some hatchetfish can "fly" for twenty feet! Actually the fish doesn't fly, but swims at great speed just below the surface of the water—and suddenly jumps right out to sail through the air for a second or two. This ability enables them to catch their prey on the wing, and helps them to be a factor in keeping down the mosquito population of many South American streams. Since the hatchetfishes are such fine jumpers, experienced aquarists know that the aquarium containing them must be kept covered at all times. Then too, feeding these little fellows is quite a problem. Ordinarily small freshwater fleas, known as Daphnia, serve as excellent food for these surface feeders, but there are times when live foods are not available and the aquarist must be resourceful to provide suitable fare for this finny pet. In such emergencies the hatchetfish usually will accept fine, floating prepared foods, such as the kinds available in cans at every pet shop.

Wanted: a Name for This Fish

Along the north-eastern section of South America there occurs a tiny brilliant tropical fish known as *Pristella riddlei*. This fish is so mild-mannered, so easily bred and so simply reared, that it has earned the love of every aquarist who has ever maintained it. Although the fish is attractive in shape and hue it has no specially outstanding trait to make it easily identifiable, and consequently has never acquired a "popular" name. Its scientific name, *Pristella*, means "saw teeth", while *riddlei* is for the collector, Oscar Riddle. Maybe the "saw-tooth tetra" might be appealing to some, maybe not. Have you a suggestion?

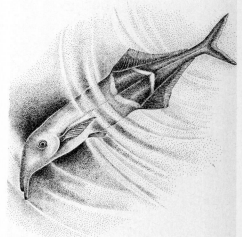

(above)
Found only in tropical Africa, the **elephant-nosed fish** is appropriately named. Although it has a rather stiff body, it is capable of swift movement when aroused.

(left)
With their tiny fins and rigid bodies, **trunkfish** can move about well but rather slowly. When handled they give off toxic secretions that may kill other fish. They must be kept alone in very large tanks.

Peaceful yet playful, the many species of **barbs** are easy to keep and breed. Their scales act like tiny mirrors, reflecting light as they dart about. Because of their excellent appetites, they are often used to clean up bits of food other fish have left.

From Argentina: a Harmony in Blood and Blue!

Now let's take a look at Argentina. This large country offers aquarists many varied and interesting fishes. First on the list should be the bloodfin, *Aphyocharax rubropinnis,* for here is a fish with blood-red fins and a slate-blue body. Its personality is nothing like so vivid as its appearance, for the fish is of extremely mild manner, though an active swimmer. The bloodfin is easily bred and a pair will often be seen spawning in the community aquarium where they go dashing about wildly through the plants, spraying eggs haphazardly in all directions. These eggs are ill-fated in the community aquarium—for the other fishes eagerly follow the breeders and gobble up the eggs as quickly as they are spawned. It goes without saying that the breeders must be removed from the other fishes if their young are to be reared.

Up to this point most of our information has been about fishes inhabiting the large rivers and lakes of the world. Did you ever consider what happens to fishes that live in small intermittent pools in the tropics? These pools are quite full and teeming with life during the height of the rainy season. But when the skies clear and the sun glares down, and the pools dry up, what happens to the fishes that lived in them? How do they get back into the pool after the pool has been dried out for a few months? Aquarists were able to answer these questions for the scientists.

A Fish That Lives Only to Lay Eggs and Die!

One of the most beautiful of such "annual" fishes (called "annual" because they usually live for one season) is the Argentine pearlfish, *Cynolebias bellotti.* In this species, as in all annuals, the male is much more beautifully marked than the female, and is usually of smaller size than his mate. These fish breed continually during the second half of their year-long lifetimes. Their breeding habits are of great interest. As the water begins to evaporate from the pools in which the fishes live, the temperature rises. Finally, the rising temperature forces the fish to stay on the bottom; and just before the pool dries they dig small depressions in the mud and lay their eggs in these before they die. The eggs are protected from the sun by the hard covering of the dried mud, and hatch out as soon as the next season's rains fill the pool.

In Africa we find a comparable situation. The yellow panchax, *Pachypanchax playfairi* and the big-eyed panchax, *Aphyosemmus bibittatum,* are also annual fishes, though they may live longer than one year in the aquarium. The eggs of these species are laid among thick vegetation or in the soft mud and take a few weeks to hatch. One interesting feature about the yellow panchax is that its scales very often stand out from its body as though the fish were diseased. This phenomenon is peculiar to this species and a satisfactory explanation is still to come.

The Congo Tetra Loses Part of Its Tail!

THOUGH AFRICAN FISHES ARE LESS COMMON in home aquaria than South American fishes, there is another extremely popular fish from the dark continent called the Congo tetra, *Phenacogrammus interruptus.* This fish comes from the Stanley pool in the Congo River system. The middle portion of the tail fin grows longer and longer until it finally breaks off. The fact that the top fin (dorsal) is longer on the male fish is merely a sexual difference; on most aquarium fishes we find that the males have longer and more pointed dorsal fins and are usually more brightly hued.

Meet the Popular Zebrafish and Its Cousin!

IF WE CONTINUE OUR TRAVELS to the East we run into some very popular aquarium fishes from the region about India. Let's meet the zebrafish, *Brachydanio rerio,* from Bengal. These fish are very fast swimmers. They are peaceful, hardy and will eat any kind of tropical fish food. They hold up well under many adverse aquarium conditions and their hues are beautiful. To these features add low price, ease of breeding, plus world-wide availability and you have the explanation of why this is, so far as sales are concerned, the most popular egg-laying fish.

A close cousin of the zebrafish is the spotted danio, *Brachydanio nigrofasciatus,* from Burma. Here again we find a fish with extremely desirable traits, and consequently the fish is very popular.

Strange as it may seem, the **mudskipper** spends most of its life almost completely out of the water. It skips over the surface of shallow pools, leaping a foot high or higher on each bound, until it reaches its destination. Frequently it sits on the roots of mangrove trees and absorbs oxygen from the water by keeping only its tail submerged.

The life span of most fishes of aquarium size is about four years, plus or minus a year. The fast-moving fishes, like the zebrafish and the spotted danio, might last only three years, but such slow-moving fishes as the goldfish might last seven or eight years.

These Relatives of Goldfish Are Interesting and Hardy

THE ABSENCE OF GOLDFISH in a tropical fish collection might seem accidental, but it is not. Goldfish are considered as truly cold-water fishes and any tropical fish hobbyist would raise his eyebrows if he saw a goldfish in with a tank of tropicals; but there is no reason why the two types of fishes should not be kept together as long as one does not eat the other.

A few very close relatives of the goldfish, the barbs, are very familiar to aquarists. The most beautiful of these are the black rubies or purple-headed barbs, *Puntius nigrofasciatus.* The obvious difference in hue of the male and female makes sex determination a simple matter. The whole genus of barbs (so called because the incorrect generic name of this group is *"Barbus"*) breeds quite like the goldfish, scattering eggs haphazardly into a mass of vegetation. The eggs hatch in a few days and the baby fish are easily raised. The usual number of fish raised from one spawning is several hundred, despite the fact that the parent fish eat half the eggs before they are finished spawning.

Prior to breeding, many fish must be brought to condition before they will spawn. This means that the female must be full of eggs, and only the obvious swelling of the female's abdomen is a sure sign of this condition. When viewed from above the shape of the female indicates her breeding condition. If her sides are bulging, she is prepared for spawning . . . if her sides are slim, she is not ready to breed. Being certain of the female's preparedness is very important, for the male can be conditioned in a few hours, and if the female is not ready to spawn he may kill her. Other barbs, like the golly barb, *Puntius oligolepis,* from Sumatra, *Puntius cummingi,* from Ceylon, and *Puntius stoliczkai,*

(above)
Today's **goldfish,** which evolved from carp, has been bred in China since the seventh century. It has thrived under conditions that would kill other species. Not a true tropical fish, it is still quite popular with aquarium owners.

(right)
When it is spawning time, the male **black ruby barb** turns a dark cherry red. Unfortunately, this sudden color change is short-lived. With mating finished the male soon loses his crimson glow, becoming once again just an ordinary striped barb.

from Burma and Thailand, all have the same breeding habits and attain the same size with a maximum of about two inches in length. There are many barbs known to aquarists, and some twenty different species are always available in well-stocked pet shops. Many hobbyists make up community collections of the various barbs, as they have contrasting hues, interesting habits and are very hardy.

A Fish You Can See Through—and One like a Bumblebee!

WHILE ON THE SUBJECT OF SOUTH ASIAN FISHES, let's take a look at some of the rarities from that corner of the world. The glassfish, *Chanda ranga* (often incorrectly called *Ambassis lala*) is one of the oddest of aquarium fishes. Delicate and glasslike in appearance, it is very hardy and is easily bred. The glassfish is a native of India and Burma, but imported specimens are rare because they are now bred commercially in huge quantities by aquarium suppliers.

Another interesting aquarium gem from the same part of the world is the bumblebeefish, *Brachygobius doriae*. The small size, short abrupt body and way in which it clings to the walls of its home are quite enough to remind one of a bumblebee; but this fish is actually marked like one as well, with black and yellow contrasting bars. In all gobies nature has fused the two ventral fins into a suction cup which permits the fish to cling to very slippery objects. This holdfast organ is more or less developed on various gobies and is a characteristic of this group. The bumblebeefish should be really considered a scavenger as it is definitely a bottom feeder and is nocturnal in its habits.

Harlequins Are the Beauties of the Aquatic World

THE MARVELLOUS HUES of the harlequinfish, *Rasbora heteromorpha*, are a match for any other harmony of natural beauty. Many hobbyists refer to this fish as "The Jewel of the Orient". Photographs can hardly capture the magnificence that a school of harlequinfish presents

(above)
Like a floating prism, the transparent **glassfish** sometimes catches the light in such a way as to reflect a rainbow of colors. Although it looks fragile, it is actually quite hardy and long-lived.

(left)
In Malaya the handsome **harlequinfish** is so plentiful that it is used as fertilizer. Outside the Orient, however, it is prized primarily for its beauty. For years a rare and expensive fish, it is now imported by the thousands.

Only the male **swordtail** has the long tail-fin extension. Careful breeding has produced beautiful, bright-hued fishes that are justifiably popular among aquarium enthusiasts.

—yet in Malaya these fish are so plentiful they are used as fertilizer in the fields.

In America it is quite a different story, for they are truly an extraordinary addition to the home aquarium. Every community aquarium should contain at least a pair of harlequinfish; they are hardy, peaceful and easy to maintain.

Fish That Lost Their Eyes in a Dark Cave

BLIND CAVE-FISH, scientifically known as *Anoptichthys jordani,* were discovered in a subterranean pool of a dark cave, now known as La Cueva Chico, in Mexico. These small silvery fish have only the most rudimentary of eyesockets. During the thousands of years the cave-fish were imprisoned in their lightless pool, they lost any use for eyes and the eyes themselves!

Thorough scientific analysis has followed this discovery of a blind fish; other blind cave-fishes have been discovered in America and Africa, and undoubtedly more will be found now that the world knows that fishes can live their entire lives in total darkness, generation after generation. How the fish got inside the cave, how they lived with apparently little natural food or green vegetation, or how they lost their eyes, are questions of interesting scientific meaning; their answers are yet to be determined.

In an aquarium these fish are active, always on the move. They do not bump into other fish, plants or rocks, and they are able to breed, eat and stay away from predatory fishes as well as most sighted species.

Scientists long ago studied the activities of blindfolded fish and discovered that they were able to find food and navigate very well, even though they obviously could not see a thing. The researchers realized there was some sort of "radar" or "sonar" system, but only in recent years has it been learned that these functions are carried out by the "lateral line". This can be plainly seen on most fishes, running from bill-cover to the tail. It seems to detect minute changes in water pressure and slight currents, but even today its method of functioning is not exactly understood.

Swordtails Are Fishes with Swords on Their Tails

IN THE SAME GENERAL AREA OF MEXICO, many years after La Cueva Chico was found, another interesting group of fishes were discovered. This group is now scientifically known as fishes of the genus *Xiphophorus*. This Greek word means "bearing a sword", but it does not refer to the swordlike extension of the caudal fin on the male swordtail. Actually the very small anal fin of most male live-bearers is modified into a sexual organ known as a "gonopodium". When this organ is viewed under a low-power microscope it looks like a sword; hence the Greek word, "bearing a sword".

The genus of fishes that has been cross-bred the most is undoubtedly the swordtail. So very many different patterns have been fixed for the fishes of this genus that no less than nineteen distinct forms are available on the market today. We find plain green swordtails; the original stock from the wild. A black band has been developed by this fish, and extends from the rear of the gill covers to the tail; aquarists call this variety a "tuxedo". Thus, a green fish with a black stripe is called a "green tuxedo swordtail".

Actually not all members of the genus *Xiphophorus* have swordtails. The fish we call "swordtails" belong to the species *helleri* usually, whereas the fish known as *Xiphophorus maculatus,* though belonging to the same genus, and freely interbreeding with *helleri,* do not have swordlike extensions on the tail fin of the male fish. These swordless swordtails are called "platies", a contraction of their old scientific name *Platypoecilus.*

A Scientist Who Develops New Kinds of Fish

THE MAN WHO DEVELOPED MOST, if not all, the varieties of platies and swordtails, and whose name is almost inevitably mentioned whenever these fishes are discussed, is Dr. Myron Gordon. This great scientist, in his huge laboratory which is located in The American Museum of Natural History in New York, studies these fishes genetically, relative to certain types of cancer. Dr. Gordon has proved by his experiments that certain cancers in fishes are hereditary; some of the most beautiful aquarium fishes in existence are a by-product of these researches.

One of Dr. Gordon's major contributions to aquarists was the de-

Wild swordtails are a rather nondescript blue-green color. This **hybrid swordtail** is one of many varieties that have been produced by means of selective breeding.

(right)
Tough-skinned and almost tailless, the **moonfish** is a variety of the platy. Its name comes from the large black, crescent-shaped patch found immediately before the stubby tail.

(below)
Because the **platy** can be successfully inbred again and again, it has been used to study the transmission of inherited traits from one generation to the next. Many strikingly vibrant color variations have been isolated.

velopment of the "wagtail" on swordtails and platies. The wagtail is a coal black pigmentation on the rays and filaments of the caudal fin. The wagtail platy is further decorated with a "tuxedo". It is one of the steps in the development of an all-black swordtail or platy. This all-black fish is far from a reality, but may come someday.

Many platies, instead of having decorated tails, have a large black crescent-shaped patch on their body, immediately before the tail. This area, called the "caudal peduncle", is found on the moonfish, a common name applied to platyfish without a tuxedo or wagtail.

As was mentioned earlier, the platies and swordtails are live-bearers. They deliver their young alive, like mammals. Just how much the mother contributes to the nourishment of her unborn offspring isn't fully known, but certainly she does not contribute as much as mammalian mothers. Actually, the eggs of the mother fish are fertilized internally by the father fish and the eggs develop internally. After about one month of internal development, the fry emerge as fully formed miniatures of their mother. The males, if they are swordtails, will develop their swords six months later.

Fishes Must "Get Along" in a Community Aquarium

THE SUCCESS OF THE COMMUNITY AQUARIUM depends upon how well the fishes get along together. Most aquarists with experience would advise the beginner to stick to the swordtails and platies, for with these fishes success is guaranteed. The swordtails and platies are so peaceful, hardy and easy to care for, that they are "a natural" for the beginner. Then again, breeding is insured, for in a tankful of female fish, some are certain to be dropping live babies every few days.

Another quality of these fish is the great variety of hues and patterns in which they are bred. Platies and swordtails, and hybrids from them, are available in three shades of red, orange, pink (albino form), gold,

(below)
Puffers, or **porcupine fish,** inflate themselves with air or water at the first sign of danger. This makes them too big for many predators to swallow.

black, blue, green, spotted, striped, blotched and plain, with every combination of these markings a distinct possibility.

Europe's Choice: the American Flagfish

ANOTHER ATTRACTIVE SPECIES is that which is known among aquarists as the American flagfish—called *Jordanella floridae,* after the state of Florida from which it comes. Though not a popular aquarium fish in America, it has captured the hearts of aquarists in other parts of the world, especially in Europe, where the fish is bred intensively. Interestingly enough, the American flagfish is an egg layer and is more closely related to the swordtails and platies than many other aquarium live-bearers.

The marine aquarium is less often encountered than the freshwater variety, largely because it requires rather more attention and, speaking generally, the hobbyist has much more to choose from in buying or catching fishes for a freshwater tank. The salt-water aquarium can contain not only fishes but many other marine invertebrates, crustacea and plants as well. Sea anemones are easily found and collected on most seacoasts, and are beautiful and unusual "flowers" for the collection. The smaller crabs, like fiddlers, are amusing to watch. Small bivalve and univalve mollusks—mussels, limpets, periwinkles and even barnacles—can be added as interesting, if temporary, inhabitants; but make certain, if one should die, that it does not lie undetected and foul the water. Sea horses are fascinating, but may prove difficult to keep (regardless of what some mail-order suppliers claim or imply).

There are several major differences between freshwater and salt-water tanks. All food for a marine aquarium must be animal in nature, but this should pose no problem. Finely chopped beef, clams, fish, worms, small crustacea, and even canned shrimp will do nicely; something is always available. The marine tank must receive considerably less light than a freshwater tank, and fish may be more sensitive to temperature changes. Tropicals and temperate species may not be kept

(bottom left)
Over the eyes of the **cowfish** are small spines, or "horns," that somewhat resemble the horns of a cow. A small member of the trunkfish family, the cowfish makes an interesting addition to a marine aquarium.

(bottom center)
Although it often comes to the surface and spews forth a stream of water, the **longnose butterfly fish** is not a true archer fish. Actually, its feeding habits are like those of other butterfly fish.

(bottom right)
Knifelike spines on either side near the base of the tail help the **surgeonfish** to protect itself. These spines, which are as sharp as a doctor's scalpel, become erect whenever danger threatens.

(top)
Wrasses are popular aquarium fishes despite the fact that they may attack each other and other fishes. At night they bury themselves in the sand and go to sleep.

(above)
Mouth development among the marine **butterfly fish** has produced some bizarre profiles, but all are basically similar. These fish probe cracks and crevices in coral reefs, searching for small animals.

together. The former require 68° to 75° water, while temperate species must be kept between 55° and 68°. Salt water can only hold eighty per cent as much oxygen as fresh, so aeration and filtration must be adequate. The tank itself must be of stainless steel, monel metal, bronze or else of all-glass construction; avoid zinc, copper and brass at all costs!

The hobbyist living near a coast where a tropical coral reef is to be found is indeed fortunate; nowhere else on earth are so many brightly attractive creatures to be found living close together. Diving with a snorkel and mask, or trading with those who do, will result in a continuing supply of beautiful specimens for your tanks.

One of the most noticeable, most common and most varied of these attractive reef fishes is the butterfly fish, of the family *Chaetodontidae*. This should not be confused with the freshwater butterfly fish of the family *Pantodontidae*. The *Chaetodontidae* are small fish, usually with a pointed or elongated snout and many small teeth. They browse the reefs picking small creatures from crevices, and some at least act as "cleaners", nibbling parasites from much larger fish. The forceps butterfly fish and an orange-striped species, the longnose butterfly fish, often come to the surface and spew forth a stream of water; this has caused them to be confused with the archer fish although they have nothing like the power, range or accuracy of the latter. The forceps is noted for its aggressive nature, especially toward its own kind. Fighting is done with the dorsal spines, which are erected and brought to bear on the other fish. These fishes must be shipped in individual containers to prevent them from killing one another. Other species are regarded as peaceful in nature, and many do well in captivity.

Whenever we see a cartoon of a tropical reef, it is almost certain to have a Moorish idol in it. This large and impressive species is regarded by many as *the* fish of the coral seas. It is usually found only in the larger and more elaborate aquaria; but even in these it is difficult to keep this species in a healthy condition. They fight with other fishes, go into shock easily, are susceptible to many diseases, and in general are hard to keep—but they are spectacular and beautiful!

The fish known as tangs, surgeonfishes, or doctorfishes form a wide-ranging and highly variable group, some member of which is found in most every shallow-sea area in the tropics. These fish have a knife-like spine on each side of the base of the tail, which can be erected in most cases and is used for defense. It can slash a man's hand quite easily and it must serve to deter attack from predatory fishes as well. In one genus there are several such spines, but they are immovable. A very common species, the yellow tang, is yellow only in the Hawaiian Islands; everywhere else in its Indo-Pacific range it is a nondescript dark brown. And the young of the blue tang are bright yellow, and change to blue in the course of their growth. Various "unicorn" or "bumphead" tangs look quite normal as youngsters, but develop projections on the forehead as they mature. The tangs are

(far left)
An elusive little fish, the **fairy bass** is seldom if ever seen either in tanks or out on the coral reefs. Rich gold and purple coloring make this rare creature an unforgettable sight.

(left)
Many of the tangs develop various protuberances with age. The blunt spear of the **unicorn tang** seems to have no particular function.

herbivorous, and as they cannot survive on a protein diet, are hard to keep in aquaria. They are most often seen in the tanks of those who live near the ocean and collect regularly, or in large scientific or commercial undertakings.

Another group of fishes that have proved difficult to keep, but which are attractive and interesting, includes the various trunkfishes. These have been well described as a "bony box with fins". The body itself is a solid, inflexible box. Fins, eyes and mouth project and can be moved to some extent, but it is at best a slow and inefficient means of propulsion; rather like paddling a large skiff with one's hands. Trunkfish are classified by the shape of the exoskeleton, whether it has three, four or five sides and angles, and whether or not there are spines over the eyes. These and their slight resemblance to horns give rise to the name "cowfish". The trunkfishes give off a toxic secretion when handled, and this can kill other fish even after the trunkfish themselves have been removed. They must be kept by themselves, or in an enormous tank, like those of public aquaria.

Somewhat similar in appearance, the puffers and porcupine-puffers or burrfish are more frequently kept by hobbyists. The sharp-nosed puffers never exceed about five inches and are particularly popular. All the puffers, when threatened, can inflate their bodies with air or water until they are two or three times their normal diameter. There is a great deal of superficial variation between the different species, and—especially in the case of the trunkfishes—between sexes, as well as between immature fishes and adults.

Some of the smaller fishes inhabiting the coral reefs of the tropical seas are very beautiful, but not too often seen since they are difficult to catch. They may or may not be hard to keep. The fairy bass or royal gramma is a strikingly beautiful warm gold and royal purple fish, and lives in dark crevices in rock and coral. Skindivers seldom even see them, and a good man with a "slurp gun" is required to catch them. They do fairly well in aquaria, but seem especially sensitive to zinc poisoning, and must not be put in a galvanized pail, for instance, for

(below)
Few fishes are so striking in appearance as the **Moorish idol.** Unfortunately, it is difficult to keep, even in a large aquarium. The young have a pair of spines at the corners of their mouths.

Of the many **wrasses** known to exist, all are beautiful and almost all are violently aggressive. They will mutilate other fishes and even those of their own race.

even a short time. They have the interesting habit of keeping their bellies toward the nearest rock surface, whether it be floor, wall or roof of a cavity.

Certainly one of the most successful and well-adapted families of small reef fishes are the wrasses, found in most of the world's tropical and temperate waters. They range from ten-foot giants to tiny, three-inch "pencilfish". Many of them are distinguished by bright hues which undergo radical changes as they grow. The common Atlantic bluehead, familiar to all Caribbean skindivers and fish-watchers, is so variable it was once thought to be no less than six different species! There is still considerable confusion in classifying wrasses, but this one error, at least, has been ironed out. The smaller wrasses are often found in marine aquaria, but have "vile dispositions" and may attack each other or other fishes. Many wrasses bury themselves in the sand at night and go to sleep. It was found that all but one of forty-eight species of Hawaiian wrasses did so; the exception formed a mucous cocoon around itself, as parrotfishes do. Many of the "cleaner" fishes, which nibble parasites from other, much larger, fishes belong to the wrasse family. This kind of activity has recently come in for a good bit of study. Certainly it is a clear example of a "truce" between hunter and hunted, with benefit to both. Wrasses as a whole are attractive, boldly and brightly patterned fish. Some, like the longnosed "bird wrasse" and "cuckoo wrasse" are truly beautiful.

Whatever kind of aquarium one considers, be it a very modest one or a very elaborate affair, for freshwater or salt-water species, and whether it is devoted to a single species, or embraces a varied collection, no one could deny it can prove to be absorbingly interesting. And this attraction is well-nigh universal! Strangers stop, look and are entranced; the hobbyist is rewarded with many hours of pleasure from his charges.

CREDITS
Color photographs and illustrations appearing in this volume were supplied by the following: Photo Researchers, Inc.; The American Museum of Natural History; Armando Curcio; Doubleday & Company, Inc.; U.S. Department of the Interior, National Park Service; and H. S. Stuttman Co., Inc.

Cover illustration and illustration on page 1099 were photographed at The American Museum of Natural History.